George Manville Fenn

The Khedive's Country

George Manville Fenn

The Khedive's Country

1st Edition | ISBN: 978-3-75237-999-0

Place of Publication: Frankfurt am Main, Germany

Year of Publication: 2020

Outlook Verlag GmbH, Germany.

Reproduction of the original.

George Manville Fenn

"The Khedive's Country"

Chapter One.

Man's oldest pursuit was undoubtedly the tilling of the soil. He may in his earliest beginnings have combined therewith a certain amount of hunting while he was waiting for his crops to grow, and was forced into seeking wild fruits and turning up and experimenting on the various forms of root, learning, too, doubtless with plenty of bitter punishment, to distinguish between the good and nutritious and the poisonous and bad.

As a matter of course, a certain amount of fighting would ensue. Wild animals would be encountered, or fellow savages would resent his intrusion upon lands where the acorns were most plentiful, or some tasty form of fungus grew. But whether from natural bent or necessity, as well as from his beginnings recorded in the ancient Book, he was a gardener, and the natural outcome of gardening was, as ideas expanded, his becoming a farmer.

The world has gone rolling on, and many changes have taken place, but these pursuits remain unaltered. The love of a garden seems to be inborn; and though probably there are children who have never longed to have one of their own, they are rarities, for of whichever sex they be, the love of this form of nature still remains.

There are those who garden or farm for pleasure, and there are those, of course, who, either on a large or small scale, cultivate the soil for profit, while the grades between are innumerable. But here in England, towards the end of such a season as we have had—one that may be surely termed a record—one is tempted to say, Where does the pleasure or the profit come in?

Certainly during the present period, or cycle, or whatever it may be termed, the English climate is deteriorating. Joined to that assertion is the patent fact that the produce of the garden and farm has largely gone down in price through the cheapness of the foreign imports thrown upon the market, and the man with small or large capital who looks forward to making a modest living out of the land, without any dreams of fortune, may well pause before proceeding to invest his bawbees, and ask himself, Where shall I go?

Thousands have debated this question for generations, with the result that the Antipodes have been turned into Anglo-Saxon farms; Van Diemen's Land has become another England, with its meadows, hedgerows, and orchards; New Zealand, the habitat of tree-fern and pine, has been transformed. Even the very surface has changed, and the land that in the past hardly boasted a four-footed animal is now rich in its cattle; while Australia, the dry and shadowless, the country of downs, has been made alive with flocks, its produce mainly tallow and wool till modern enterprise and chemistry rendered it possible for the frozen mutton to reach England untainted after its long voyage across the tropics to our homes.

To keep to the temperate or cold regions, the name of Canada or the great North-West springs up as does the corn which fills our granaries; while the more enterprising cultivators of the soil, who have had souls above the ordinary plodding of the farmer's life—the fancy tillers, so to speak—with the tendency towards gardening, produced our sugar from the West Indies and British Guiana, and tobacco and cotton from the Southern States, long ere the Stars and Stripes waved overhead; while, to journey eastward, the gardens have flourished in India and Ceylon with indigo, spices, and coffee; and later on, wherever suitable slopes and terraces were found, the Briton has planted the attractive glossy-leaved tea shrub, until the trade with China for its fragrant popular produce has waned.

There are plenty of lands of promise for the cultivator, unfortunately too often speculative and burdened by doubt. They are frequently handicapped by distance, extremes of climate, and unsuitability to the British constitution. As in the past, too, imagination often plays its part, and the would-be emigrant hankers after something new, in spite of the cloud of possible failure that may hover on his horizon.

There is, of course, a great attraction in the unknown, and untried novelty is always tempting. But, on the other side, there is the old and safe, the cultivation of a land which in the past has been world-famed for its never-failing produce, its mighty granaries, and its vast fertility, that can be traced back for thousands of years, whose soil, far from becoming exhausted, is ever being renewed, and which at the present time is undergoing a transformation that will make its produce manifold.

Of course, the country which contains these qualities is the familiar old land of Egypt, the dominion of the Khedive, which, in spite of its wondrous fertility, has had little attraction for the earnest cultivator of the earth. It has been the granary of the world for ages; but its cultivation has been left to its own people, who have gone on with their old-time barbaric tillage, leaving Nature, in her lavish bounteousness, to do the rest.

In every way wonderful changes are coming over Egypt, where for countless ages the policy of the people seemed to be devoted entirely, as far as the vegetable world was concerned, to the growth of food, or such fibrous plants as proved their suitability for the manufacture of the light clothing they required. Any attempt to permanently beautify the country by taking advantage of its fertility, and commencing the planting to any great extent of that which was so lacking in the shape of trees, was left in abeyance till the coming into power of the great ancestor of the present Khedive, Mehemet Ali. This thinker, of broad intellect, made some beginnings in this direction, and later on Ismail Pacha gave a great impetus thereto by enlisting the services of a clever French gardener, who, fully awakened at once to the possibilities of climate and land, and with ideas running very much in favour of landscape gardening, began to introduce and encourage the growth of shade trees, a complete novelty in a country where the ideas of the people seem to tend towards placing their dwellings in the full glare of the sun.

Gardens began to spring up, trees were planted in suitable places, and the start having been once fairly made, the love of imitation led to the establishment of a taste or fashion, and planting has now gone on to such an extent that there are those who are ready to assert that while the face of Egypt is becoming changed, the presence of the rapidly-growing and increasing trees is having its effect, through the attraction and formation of clouds, upon the meteorology of the country. If this continues, as it may, to a vast extent, the fertility of Egypt will no longer be confined to the narrow strips on either side of the Nile, but its deserts may become physical features of the past.

The idea of those in olden times was to pile up huge erections and to let what came spontaneously grow as was its wont. Now the enlightenment of the new rulers and the leavening of Western civilisation are working wonders. That to which Ismail Pacha gave such a fillip is being fostered and advanced by the present Khedive, and, the ball being well set rolling, his people are finding out that nearly everything that loves moisture and sunshine will grow prodigiously. It takes time, of course, but many of the beautiful shade trees that have been planted have in forty years reached a height of eighty feet, and become rich in their heavy foliage. The varieties of the eucalyptus, not always the most beautiful of trees from their greyish leafage and want of shadow, are still a wonderful addition to a dry and thirsty land. Considering their original habitat in Australia, it was a foregone conclusion that they would do well here, and they have proved to be most rapid of growth.

Then there is the magnificent Flamboyer des Indes, and scores of other beautiful children of Nature, which only required care and fostering in their tender years to prove their liking for their new home. Endless are the trees that, once given a start, leave behind their scrubby, starved appearance, and become in maturity well able to care for themselves and beautify the prospect on every hand.

Acacias, with their perfumed blossoms; the deep green shady sycamore, that good old favourite like the plane of the Levant; the feathery tamarisk, and scores of ornamental trees, flourish well; while, combining the ornamental with the useful, there is the fine, slow-growing old mulberry, with its rich juicy fruit, and its suggestions of the soft straw-coloured or golden yellow rustling silk; for if ever there was a country favoured by Nature, in its dryness and absence of rain, for the prosperity of the caterpillar of the silkworm moth, it should be Egypt, where enterprise and a sensible use of capital ought to leave Asia and Turkey in Europe behind.

Leaving trees and turning to flowers, gardens in Egypt can be made, and are made, perfect paradises in the meaning of old Gerard and Parkinson; for the country is a very rosery, where the modern decorative sorts bloom well in company with the more highly scented old-fashioned kinds largely cultivated for the distillation of that wonderfully persistent essential oil, the otto or attar of roses.

Here the lover of a garden and of exotics can dispense with conservatory or the protection of glass, and, giving attention to moisture and shade, make his garden flush ruddily with the poinsettia, and may also find endless pleasure in the cultivation of some of the more beautiful varieties of the orchid family, which here in England demand the assistance of a stove.

Perhaps the most attractive time for the visitor from England, who has thoughts of settling in this country, to see it at its best is when the Nile is rising to its height, bringing down from Equatorial regions its full flow of riches and the means of supplying the cultivator with that which will reward him for his labours beneath the torrid sun.

At this time the crops are approaching maturity; the vast fields of maize have been passing through the various stages of green, waving, flag-like leaf, and hidden immature cob, with its beautiful, delicate tassel, prelude of the golden amber or black treasure that is to come and gladden the eye of the spectator in every direction. The grassy millet, or *dourra*, is equally beautiful in its wavy-wind-swept tracts; the cotton crops are gathering strength prior to the swelling and bursting of the silky boll; and the majestic sugar-cane towers up in its rapid progress, till the whole country is smiling in preparation for the gladsome laughter of the harvest that is to come, for it has been a busy time. The fellaheen, in their thousands, have been occupied in that wonderful irrigation which has been the careful distribution through meandering canal, straight-cut dyke, and endless little rill, of the lurid thick water of the Nile, laden with its rich plant-sustaining fertility, to the roots of the thirsty plants, and stimulating them beneath the ardent sunshine into a growth that is almost startling. In other parts the same waters are being ingeniously led to the cultivated lands that are being made ready for the more ordinary grain crops—the wheat, the homely barley, and the Egyptian bean, the food of man and beast alike; while in a country where grassy down and ordinary meadow, such as form the pasture of sheep, oxen and kine at home, are unknown, tract upon tract is annually sown with Egyptian clover, lentils, and similar crops— ready for immediate use as cattle food in which the animals can graze bit by bit as far as their tethering lines will permit—for cutting and stacking up green in the form of ensilage, and consumption when the crops are past—or for hay.

THE NILE IN FLOOD.

The granary of the world, the vast store-house for nations: people have gone there to buy, but not to till; and yet it presents so many qualities that the wonder is that it should have been so long neglected; while now, in its state of transformation through the opening of the great dam and the cutting and forming of miles more irrigating canal, there is no bound to what may be done in the future. The time seems to be approaching when Egypt will no longer be spoken of as a narrow strip of fertile soil running from north to south and bordering the Nile, for its future seems to be that the barren sand far back from its banks will be turned into fertile land, adding its produce of corn and cotton to the store-house of the world.

As is well-known, vast tracts of Egypt are by nature sterile; but upon these barren primaeval sands there has been superimposed for uncountable ages the alluvium of the Nile, so that, as an old writer says, Egypt itself may be looked upon as the gift of one of the mightiest rivers of the world. He speaks of the Nile as being the father of this country, bounteous in its gift, a strange, mysterious, solitary stream which bears down in its bosom the riches of the interior of Africa, carrying onward from far away south the fertility of the luxuriant tropics, and turning the sterile sand into the richest soil of the world. It is this richness of the south that has changed the Delta from an arid waste into a scene of matchless beauty.

One gazes upon it from the summit of one of the pyramids or some high citadel, over cities and ruins of cities, palm grove, green savannah, palace and garden, luxuriant cornfield, and olive grove. Far distant, shimmering in a silvery haze and stretching away into the dimness of the horizon, lies the boundless desert, now being rapidly reclaimed, consequent upon the great barrage experiments for the supplying of the many winding canals with the fertile waters of the parent river. And of these still growing distributors of life, these bearers of commerce, the numbers are almost beyond belief. They are the veins and arteries of the country, depositing as they do the rich soil which furnishes abundance, and then acting as the waterways upon which, in due time, the harvests are borne throughout the length and breadth of the land.

There is a great discrepancy in the reports as to the number of these canals, and statements made and chronicled a few years back are not of much use as statistics at the present day; while the completion of the great dam will give such an impulse to their formation that the mileage, even if properly estimated now, will be useless as a basis ten years hence.

One traveller, in his ignorance of the country, estimated the number of these irrigating water distributors as only ninety, while another of about the same date gives Upper Egypt alone six thousand. Probably, though, in this instance he included every branch and branchlet that led the water amongst the cultivated lands.

The water of these canals, renewed as it is by the annual risings of the

Nile, goes on steadily changing, wherever it is led, the primaeval sand of the desert into rich deep soil, after the fashion, but on a grander scale, of the ingenious way in which portions of fen and bog land in north Lincolnshire and south Yorkshire have been transformed into fertile farms. As compared to what is going on in Egypt, this process is trivial in the extreme; but by man's forethought and ingenuity many a peat bog and waste that aforetime grew nothing but reed and rush has been made, by draining and leading upon it the muddy waters of the Ouse, Trent, and their tidal tributaries, into rich and prosperous farms, producers of the necessities of life. These warp farms, as they are termed, stand high in favour with the cultivators of the soil. They have taken years to produce, perhaps, and the process has consisted of but one treatment.

In Egypt, on the contrary, this depositing of the rich mud goes on year by year, adding fresh soil and additional fertility each season; and the possibilities of increase are almost without limit; while the drainage produced by the falling of the Nile, the sandy subsoil, and the wonderful evaporation of this sunny, almost rainless land, entirely preclude the newly fertilised tracts becoming sour and stale.

Those interested should know somewhat of the constituents of this Nile mud, which is brought down from the south to be deposited, it must be borne in mind, upon sand which in the course of cultivation will naturally, as it is mingled with the mud, render it open, porous, and highly suitable for vegetable growth. A rough analysis proves that quite half of the deposit is argillaceous, or clayey earth, one fourth carbonate of lime. These constituents alone should be sufficient to gladden the heart of any farmer or gardener, without counting the iron, carbonate of magnesia, and silica.

So many of our agricultural outposts are only to be reached by long and tedious journeys across ocean and then inland. Egypt is, of course, in Africa, but only a few days' journey from our own shores. The sea transit is short and frequent; and the country, the ancient mysterious land of the Dark Ages, is rapidly being opened out by rail. The climate, in spite of the heat, is one of the finest in the world, and its healthiness is proverbial; while, best of all for the would-be adventurer, it is under an enlightened rule, beneath which progress and civilisation are flourishing more and more.

Chapter Two.

Reports from the highest quarters supply abundant statistics of the great advantage already manifested by the completion of the Nile Barrage. The increase of land available for culture through the conservation of the water that has always run to waste, and the augmented powers supplied for irrigation by holding up such vast bodies of water, have resulted in returns that are striking in the extreme, and this after so short a time has elapsed since the sluices were completed and the great dams put to the test. The value of land and rentals have gone up, water has been utilised at earlier dates than were customary of old, and everything points not only to stability but to a future for Egypt such as could not have been dreamed of a score of years ago. In connection, therefore, with its future prospects from an agricultural point of view, and the encouragement given by the Government to those who are disposed to enter upon a business career in this favoured country, so as to bring to bear experience, the knowledge of culture, and the use of improved implements to add vastly to Egypt's produce, a short sketch of what has been done by one whose faith in the delta as a vast agricultural centre has always been strong, will not here be out of place.

We allude to the efforts made by his Highness the Khedive in acquiring and reclaiming tracts of land in the neighbourhood of Cairo and turning them into fertile farms.

A trip to one of these nearest to Cairo struck a visitor directly as being hall-marked by the stamp "Progress," for it was reached by a little model railway which skirts his Highness's estates. After leaving the station, a short drive brings the visitor almost at once to a series of scenes indicating careful management and model farming, though there is much in it that is novel to an English eye, consequent on its being contrived to suit the exigencies of an Eastern country where but little rain is known to fall.

OXEN AND NATIVE PLOUGH.

One of the first objects reached upon entering the cultivated land was the great granary or store, composed of spacious erections of but one storey high, low-roofed, and enclosing a large central square. In some of these buildings were stored up sacks of corn, while in others lay large heaps of the newly picked cotton, of whose cultivation more will be said elsewhere.

The land around this highly cultivated domain is very fertile, and the air exhilarating; and at present it is letting at the rate of 10 pounds per feddan, which represents the Egyptian acre, something larger than our own. This is the present price, for enterprise so far has done little upon this side of Cairo in the shape of market gardening, although the district is only twelve minutes by rail from the centre of this important city, and one hour's distance for a walking horse and cart.

MODERN CULTIVATOR AND OLD-WORLD YOKE.

Attached to the building above referred to were well-erected ranges of cattle-sheds, not occupied for fattening purposes, but for the culture of the farm, this culture being carried on not by horses, but by oxen— buffaloes and ordinary bullocks—which are regularly used, as at one time in Old England, yoked to the plough, harrow, or roller, and on some of the high grounds which are let by his Highness, for turning the water-wheels, though on the model farms steam power only is used for the purposes of irrigation.

These sheds are built in the same fashion as the granary, a noteworthy point in connection with the big, sleek, well-fed occupants being that instead of, as in English fashion, standing in one long row with their backs to the visitor, they are ranged in ranks, fifty-six in all, sideways to the spectator, facing so many feeding troughs, and each provided with its tethering halter and a sliding iron ring attached to an iron bar, giving freedom to each animal to stand or lie down at its pleasure without any risk of self-inflicted injury.

As a specimen of the model-farm-like erection of these buildings, it may be stated that the feeding troughs are of solid masonry, made impervious and clean by an inner lining of zinc. No partitions are used to separate these draught cattle, but by the arrangement of the haltering they can be kept at such a distance that no two could come into contact. Everything was beautifully clean, the great animals being amply supplied with dry earth for litter, its disinfecting qualities being admirable from a cleanly point of view, and valuable for the purposes of the farm.

One of the principal foods for cattle upon the farm is *Tibn*, as it is called by the Egyptians—chopped or bruised straw, made more nutritious, according to the needs of the animal in feeding, by the addition of beans or barley; and in the progress across the place a huge stack of this chaff-like provender was passed, some ten feet high, but totally unprotected from the weather by thatch. The reply to questions by the manager was simple in the extreme, yet in itself a chapter on the beautiful nature of the climate. The reason why the stack had no protecting thatch was that there was no need, the rain was so trifling, and when the wind and its habit of scattering stacks was mentioned, the inquirer was told that it did no harm.

In passing one enclosure sheep were encountered—a class of farming, as stated elsewhere, little affected on account of the absence of grass downs and ordinary grazing fields; but these were in a healthy, flourishing state, well fleeced, with a fine white semi-transparent-looking wool, indicating relationship to the Angora breed, specimens of the latter being seen later on in fold.

Some of the fields had been devoted to the growth of cotton. This had lately been picked and transferred to the great store, the wood of the beautiful plant so stored being yet upon the ground waiting for transfer to the stacks for fuel purposes, it being utilised for the steam engines used upon the farm, especially for working the water-raising machinery so extensively needed in this occasionally thirsty land.

Farther on an implement was being used in preparing fields for irrigation; and as in its simplicity of construction it was dragged over the great enclosure, it drew up the well-tilled, friable soil into ridges or slightly raised portions whose object was to regulate the flow of irrigating water equally all over the field, so that when it was flooded no portion should get more than its due share, one part being swamped while another would be comparatively dry. Simple in the extreme in its construction, as the illustration shows, the implement was thoroughly efficient in the way in which it did its work, with but slight exertion on the part of the sluggish oxen by which it was drawn.

All this was novel, yet paradoxically old-world and strange, but in the next field there was a combination of the old and new—a pair of oxen used as in Saxon times, and down to not so many years back even near London, patiently plodding along beneath their yoke and drawing an emanation from our Eastern counties in the shape of a Ransome and Sims' harrow, light and effective, apparently as much at home and progressing as easily as if on a Suffolk farm.

There was a familiarity about these fields which took off the dead monotony of the level, for they were surrounded by good-sized, well-grown trees, whose aspect betokened health and a suitability of climate, while on a nearer approach they showed their foreignness to the soil, proving to be a variety of the well-known Siberian crab, or cherry apple, beloved of boys, but here grown in such bulk as to suggest being used for crushing and utilising in some special way.

One thing that strikes the European in Egypt, when passing beyond the more carefully cultivated portions near the city, is the absence of trees other than the indigenous palms; but here, in these newly-reclaimed portions, much has been done, as already mentioned, in the way of planting. For instance, the approaches to a range of buildings in connection with this farm were studded with acacias, ornamenting what proved to be the pigeon houses which are such a regular adjunct to an Egyptian cultivator's home. Their occupants bear a strong resemblance to our own blue rocks, or wood pigeons. Another building was the dairy farmhouse, well-built, simple, and most suitable; while in the neighbouring fields the cows were pasturing after the economical plan carried out in our Channel Islands—where each milk-producer is not allowed to wander through and waste the precious herbage at her own sweet will, but is tethered to a stake—while the calves had an enclosure to themselves. Here were many examples of experiments being tried to improve the breed, the favourite animal being a cross between the Swiss—Fribourg—and native; and in this cross-breeding only those proved to be advantageous are retained. Such as do not show some marked advance upon the native stock, either for breeding or the production of milk, are sold.

One very fine sire was close at hand—a Swiss bull with a noble head and short curved horns, fine and long of coat, which about brow and neck formed itself into short, crisp curls like those that cluster upon the brow of the classic Hercules. This grand animal greatly resembled, save that it was much larger, one of the choice and jealously guarded patriarchs of a Jersey cattle-shed; while his home-like aspect was added to greatly by the familiar ring in the nose, which is not considered necessary for the native animals.

A little farther on were those rather uncouth-looking, heavily-horned animals, the buffaloes, which run side by side in Egyptian estimation with the ordinary cattle for all practical purposes. The improvement in their breed is also studied by the addition of fresh blood and the choice of sires remarkable for special qualities. One particularly good specimen was pointed out, distinguished by the heavy hump forward, a fine beast lately brought from the Soudan.

There are two distinct breeds of buffalo utilised in this country—the productions of Upper and Lower Egypt, those from the latter district being reckoned the better.

In this portion of the farm and around the buildings fruit trees were plentiful, diversifying the scene and adding greatly to its attractiveness, and looking novel to a visitor from Europe, who saw an abundant growth of the Seville or bitter orange, and the cool, greeny-grey picturesque olive of Southern Europe and the East.

Among other fruit trees seen here were some bearing long pods, called *chiar shambar* by the natives. The fruit of these trees, which is long and green, but which turns black soon after picking, seemed at a distance like a huge bean, suggesting that the fruit was akin to the carob or locust bean, this idea being emphasised by the sweet glutinous pulp in which the seeds were buried. This pulp is pleasant to the taste, but slightly bitter, and is largely used by the natives boiled up with water, as a drink on account of its medicinal qualities.

Taken all in all, the visit to the Khedive's farm was most attractive, and pregnant with proofs of the fertility of the well-tended land, for on every side were examples of the successful culture of many of the agricultural products treated of in detail from the notes of the student-like superintendent, who has all in his charge.

The place, as before said, may be regarded as a model and example of what can be done with land that has been looked upon for ages as so much desert, when all that was required was industry, application, and the ingenuity necessary for extending the action of the Nile flood. Nature has always been ready to do the rest.

The Khedive has another tract of farm land, which he purchased some time back, about two kilometres from the estate just described, at Koubbeh. This is Mostorod, where he has a simple-looking villa. On the way here one of the first things that attract the attention of an Englishman is that home-like contrivance so often missing in foreign countries—a hedge dividing the fields from the roadway and separating them from each other. These were unknown before the time of Abbas Helmi the Second, and what may be done in time to come in the surroundings of farms by means of the simple, well cut back hawthorn remains to be proved. Here the shrubby growth, chosen for its neat form and comparatively rapid development, is the bitter orange.

At Mostorod many of the surroundings are marked by the energetic proceedings of the practical farmer. Here steam is at work, like the patient slave it is, forming the motive power in one case for raising water for all farming purposes, in another setting in action the mills, which rapidly turn out and clean the meal ground from wheat and Indian corn.

Buildings are here containing the various grains and seeds; others are the storehouses for one or other of the three pickings produced in the cultivation of cotton; and at the entrance of every building, just inside the door, there is a pitch pine wood frame, with its glass covering, and a paper on which is a record of the amount and nature of whatever is brought in or taken out of the building in the shape of corn, cotton, seed, or whatever may be stored.

Here, in opposition to much that is modern, there is a large, old-fashioned Egyptian stable, very thick of wall. The building is divided into two chambers, connected and lit from overhead, the light coming through the roof of wood and rafters thickly thatched with reeds.

These rafters are supported by thick round columns formed of the ancient, sun-dried brick for which Egypt has long been famed. Near by something of the old-world fashion of the place was visible in a typical grinding mill such as may be seen in common use in pretty well every village. It had a chamber to itself, and differed little from those which might have been seen in England fifty or a hundred years ago, set in action by an often blindfolded horse, but here worked by a bullock.

Ornamentation is not wanting at Mostorod, for the villa has its garden brightened by fruit trees, and the pillar-stemmed palms, with their leafy crowns, are frequent objects in the transparent, sunny air.

Close at hand is the village on the Khedivial estate. In it the streets are narrow and the houses of one height, thoroughly waterproof, and of the familiar construction, of sun-dried bricks covered with white plaster, and, being of an earlier date in the improvement the Khedive is striving for in the poorer class dwellings, not to be compared with the spick and span new houses he has lately had erected at Mariout, not far from Alexandria.

Hard by this village is a very large barn or stack yard with more native pigeon houses, the whole of the surroundings being extremely quaint and picturesque.

Again, a short distance onward stands the native village of Mostorod, with its attractive little mosque and a tomb erected to the memory of a saint.

The Ismailia Canal supplies water to the Koubbeh and Mostorod estates, and in this neighbourhood is a good deal of very valuable agricultural land, some portions of which are let to the fellaheen for three months in a year, so as to enable them to grow a crop of maize.

Hereabouts, tethered in the clover fields, a herd of the Khedive's camels are pastured, many of these being bred for carrying purposes, others (the slighter of build) for riding and speed. The scene is attractive from its verdure, but comparatively treeless, though it is worthy of mention that two solitary weeping willows do their best to adorn the landscape—a plain with the suggestions of home in the shape of lapwings, or birds bearing a very strong resemblance, which fly up here and there.

This estate is close to Heliopolis—the ancient On—where almost the only suggestions of the City of the Sun are the sunshine and a great square piece of white stone, bearing hieroglyphs, and in perfect preservation, while in the distance stands up in solitary state the far-famed Obelisk.

Chapter Three.

"Words, words, words!" quoth Hamlet, and the reader of this sketch of the possibilities in the way of cultivation offered by the Khedive's dominions may be disposed to contemptuously say the same. But in the following pages it is proposed to give proof of what may be done in an ordinary way by one who is gardener for pleasure and health, supplier of ordinary produce to the market, or farmer upon a larger scale, without looking for a moment upon the vast increase that is bound to follow the wider and wider distribution of that life of such a land—abundant water, not merely for irrigation, but in this case charged year by year with the rich fertilising mud of the vast equatorial regions regularly borne down by the Nile in flood.

CAMELS IN PASTURE.

Among the first questions an intending settler might ask respecting the country that he intends to make his temporary or future home would naturally be, "What is the place like? What sort of seasons are they?"

Egypt is a country which may be said to be blessed with four seasons. There is that which begins in July with the inundation of the Nile, when for about two months the whole country of the Delta may be likened to a vast lake dotted with islands represented by the towns and villages. Naturally, then, the air is moist, and mornings and evenings have their mists. In the second season, answering to our winter and early spring, we have cold nights; but the days are hot, and the vegetation is rapid and luxuriant. The third, corresponding to our spring, is the least attractive; while the fourth, which continues until the rising of the Nile, is in the highest degree delightful.

Everyone has praised the Egyptian nights—cloudless skies, an intensely bright moon, so bright that at harvest time, for reasons in connection with the shedding of the grain, it is the custom amongst the farmers and cultivators of the soil to take advantage of the coolness and light to commence garnering their crops at midnight. So bright is the moon in this extraordinarily clear atmosphere that the peasantry

18

who sleep in the open air are careful to shade their eyes from the rays, which are often said to produce a more painful effect than those of the sun.

These pages contain the experience of long years of patient study of the cultivation of Egypt, of that carried on by the native, who for ages past has looked to the soil for his sustenance. And of his practical knowledge, that which is valuable has been adopted; while experiment, experience, and the effects of modern cultivation have run with it side by side.

Every gardener and farmer knows, however enlightened he may be and fond of the modern ways of doing things, that it is not wise to look slightingly upon old-fashioned customs. *Experientia docet* is a well-known maxim, and the experience taught often by generations of disappointments is worthy of all respect.

Men go on cultivating and growing certain things which excite the contempt of a stranger, but too often he lives to learn that there was good reason for the practice, hence, animated by the spirit of respect for the old, while striving to introduce the new and improved, the notes and descriptions herein contained may be depended upon as being thoroughly practical and well worthy the attention of every cultivator who has at heart the future of the Delta and the higher irrigated lands of Egypt.

Further, it may be presumed that every reader is fully acquainted with the fact that lower Egypt possesses a climate without extreme variations of temperature; that winter is hardly known but as a name; and that, though changes have taken place of late years, probably from increased cultivation and planting, the rainfall is extremely small. And yet the fertility of Egypt is proverbial, and due to this annual flooding of the lands by the Nile, which—after the fashion, already referred to, of the northern midlands of England, where so many acres have been flooded and drained after a lengthened deposit of mud, or "warp," as it is termed—become rich in the extreme. The warping in Yorkshire and Lincolnshire is an artificial and protracted process, carried out once only; the warping of the land of Egypt is natural, and repeated year by year; while as soon as the water has run off, the coating of mud, rich in all the qualities of fertility, is ready to bear, after the merest scratching of the soil, its abundant one, two, or even three crops in a year.

Here are possibilities, then, for the cultivator who is ready to bring to bear all the appliances of modern science, the discoveries of practical agricultural chemistry, and, above all, the mechanical and ingenious inventions so admirable in a flat, open country, unbroken by hedge or tree.

Among the minor objects familiar to the tourist in his journey up the Nile are the various means of raising water for the irrigation of the crops. These have been, and still continue to be in many places extremely primitive, for, as before stated, the fellaheen in their conservative fashion are prone to cling to the inventions of their forefathers. Hence they may still be seen laboriously at work with their shadoofs, sakiehs, and other water-wheels worked by hand or mule power, raising the fertilising fluid to a sufficient height to be discharged and flow of itself, spreading over the patches of land requiring irrigation.

But these clumsy contrivances are giving place in the newly-reclaimed and cultivated parts of the Delta to modern machinery, urged by motive power, notably by steam, though to a great extent advantage is taken of the wind; for it is a common thing to see in the landscape the circular disc-like object, as noted at a distance, formed by a windmill with its many fans, or "vans," standing at the edge of some canal or by one of the many wells that have been dug upon the higher grounds.

For though tract after tract may be desert, presenting nothing but coarse growth and sand ready to drift before the wind, there is not much difficulty in finding water, notably in the wide plateau known as Mariout, spreading out in the direction of the Libyan Desert from Alexandria. Here the sinking of wells results in the finding of water at depths varying from twenty to forty feet, and boring to a greater depth would doubtless produce a fuller supply, for in so flat and porous a land, within easy measurable distance of the great inland sea, there is every probability that an inexhaustible supply is within touch. And nowadays the various ingenious contrivances of the mechanical engineer are always ready, and at small cost, to supplement during the dry times the abundant supply offered by the great river. Of course, this deals solely with the higher grounds that are not reached without mechanical help by the dam-supplied network of canals that already veins the country, and projects for the increase of which are, since the opening of the great works at Assiout and Assouan, either under consideration, or already planned.

WIND AND WATER.

The slow, clumsy hand labour of the shadoof and the awkward cattle-worked sakieh, or earthen pot surrounded water-wheel, is now being superseded in the larger tracts of cultivation by such ingenious pieces of mechanism as the centrifugal pump, worked by steam, and so contrived that it can be utilised on the bank of river or canal, and with a suction tube turned down at any angle, so that it can be lowered into any of the common wells that are sunk in all directions. The portable

21

steam engine used in connection therewith is one of the grandest slaves of civilisation, playing its part on the large farms for traction, threshing, straw chopping, or other of the many necessities of cultivation. By means of these centrifugal pumps after the middle of November on large estates the water has to be forced into the service (estate) canals.

A ten-horse power engine, driving a ten-inch pump, will irrigate the same number of acres in twelve hours, lifting the water five feet, the cost of raising water being two shillings per acre. The small occupiers of land sometimes raise their supply from wells and canals by means of Persian wheels or Archimedean screws.

Chapter Four.

At Cairo when the Nile commences its annual rise, for the first few days its tint seems to be green; but the general tone during the inundation is of a dirty red, of course due to its being thickened with the mud brought down from the south. During this rising, irrigation can be sent freely flowing over all cultivated lands, as the river continues about the level of the banks till the middle of November.

In simple language, irrigation means the turning of desert into richly fertile producing land. A great deal has been said and done, but everything points to the fact that, however great and productive a garden Egypt has been for countless years, it is still almost, as it were, in its infancy. The erection of that stupendous piece of engineering, the Assouan Dam, has already had effects that have surpassed the expectations of its projectors; and writing upon this subject, Sir William Willcocks, a gentleman whose knowledge of the position is of the highest value, points out a series of facts that are almost startling in their suggestions. He draws attention to the fact that there are still two million acres of excellent land waiting to be reclaimed after the simple fashion herein described, and then requiring to be irrigated to the full extent needed—that is to say, perennially.

These are large figures to deal with, but Egypt is a vast country, and its powers of production almost beyond belief; but everything is bound up in the one need—water supply; and it is this furnishing of life to plants, and enabling them to find it latent, as it were, in the far-spreading plains that are as yet but sand and dust, that is taking the attention of our great engineers.

Here they find room to exert their powers. It is only a year ago that we had the inauguration of the first great stride; and now we are told that the thirsty country asks for more. To fully carry out the perennial irrigation that shall fertilise the two million acres still waiting, "the country requires one milliard of cubic metres of water per five hundred thousand acres"—that is to say, four times that quantity. At the present time, with the height to which it has been already erected, the Assouan Dam holds up and supplies one milliard of these cubic metres of water in all, a sufficiency for five hundred thousand acres of agricultural and garden land. It is proposed to raise it twenty-one feet higher, with the result that its holding powers will be so vastly increased that the supply will be doubled, and hence be sufficient for another five hundred thousand acres. But even then there will be a milliard acres still waiting for a supply of water to the extent of two milliards of cubic metres of water for themselves. Whence is this supply to come?

The engineers are ready with their answer, and only ask for the capital, not to float some mad scheme, but to spread bounteously the rich water which turns, as above said, the desert into fertile land.

The plan, or project, is to form a huge reservoir in the Wady Rayan, which will with ease supply the water needed at a cost of about two million pounds—a large sum of money, but ridiculously small in comparison with the results. There is, however, a drawback in connection with this reservoir—a weakness, so to speak, which alone would render its value questionable, for while in April and May, during the flood time, its supply would be enormous, it would fall off very much in June, and furnish but very little in July.

But now in connection therewith we find the truth of the old proverbial saying, "Co-operation is strength." Alone it would be weak, but if made now and worked in connection with the Assouan Reservoir it becomes strong, and the two being tapped in turn as the need arose, the combination would have tremendous results, one reservoir so helping the other that sufficient water could be depended upon to keep up a perennial supply.

To give Sir William Willcocks' words:

> Let us now imagine that both reservoirs are full of water, and it is April 1st. The Wady Rayan Reservoir will be opened on to the Nile and give all the water needed in that month, while the Assouan Reservoir will be maintained at its full level. In May the Wady Rayan Reservoir will give nearly the whole supply, and the

Assouan Reservoir will give a little. In June the Wady Rayan Reservoir will give a small part of the supply, and the Assouan Reservoir will give the greater part. In July the Wady Rayan Reservoir will give nothing, and the Assouan Reservoir will give the whole supply required. Working together in this harmonious and beautiful manner, these reservoirs, which are the true complements of each other will easily provide the whole of the water needed for Egypt.

Now, this raising of the Assouan Dam to the height proposed means an expenditure of five hundred thousand pounds, and the time for the completion of this addition and raising of the works two years, at the end of which period, as we have seen, its power for irrigation will be doubled; while to make the additional reservoir, and enable it to discharge its vast extra supply at the cost named, will take three years; four years will then be required to bring the water to its proper height— seven years in all; so that in that time full arrangements can be made for the perennial irrigation of the whole of Egypt.

Huge sums of money these to spend or put into the soil, two millions and a half sterling; but let us see what there is to be said on the credit side.

Take one point alone. The increase in the cotton crop of Egypt would be most extensive, and its value enormous. Then there is the land itself. Here we have so many extra acres, only partially irrigated, but which by this raising of the supply of water will be changed from partial supply land into constant—that is, each acre will be enabled to tap the reservoirs at all times of the year, according to the cultivator's need, with the consequent rise in value of the land of thirty pounds per feddan, or acre; and that means, according to Sir William Willcocks, an increase in the wealth of Egypt to the extent of sixty million pounds.

From one bold stroke! Sixty million pounds for the expenditure of five. Not bad, this, for the engineers. But still, it is but the beginning of what may be done in the Khedive's country, for it is full of suggestions to be carried out by an enterprising people for the making of the native and those of our own country who are prepared to look far ahead. The amount of land to be reclaimed is enormous; and what land! For countless ages the Nile has flowed down, bringing with it its fertile mud, depositing some by the way, carrying other some out to sea, to be lost in the depths of the Mediterranean; but still, as time rolled on, adding to, and raising higher, the huge Delta through which the various mouths made their way; so that in these lowest portions of Egypt the depth of rich soil must be enormous.

Here lie the lakes and canals of olden formation, shallowed and choked with mud, and rendered almost impassable for transit, but only waiting for the engineers to contrive modern works, the result of survey and level, feeding canals and the forming of reservoirs to supply irrigation water for freeing the land of its salt, making easy the navigation of the district, and simplifying the conveyance of its grain and other crops.

All this development is awaiting enterprise and capital low down in the Delta. But the engineers have not stopped near home and the Khedive's capital; they have cast their eyes afar across that vast extent of barbarism, the re-conquered Soudan, where, bordering upon the Nile, it is often "water, water everywhere, and not a drop" for the crops to drink.

Sir William Garstin has been busy here, surveying and examining what can be done towards and beyond Khartoum. Here rich tracts of fertile land are lying on both sides of the Blue Nile, to the extent, roughly speaking, of some three millions of acres. This land of Upper Egypt is as rich in its capabilities as that of the Delta; but it has qualities which the latter does not possess, and is more suitable for the production of excellent cotton, which can be sown as a flood crop and reaped in winter, an advantage which the seasons will not permit in Egypt.

Here, again, then, is an opening for enterprise and capital in the future, for it must not be forgotten that the Suakin-Berber Railway, well in progress, opens up this part of the country, one which some of these days will be brought well in touch with Liverpool and the northern manufacturing towns, as the cotton-growing capabilities of Upper Egypt extend.

Chapter Five.

In a country which depends upon floods and their deposit for its fertility, one of the first questions likely to be asked by a practical man is, What about the drains? He knows perfectly well, from reading and report, that the evaporation of the waters that have for the time being turned vast tracts of land literally into swamps must be enormous, but at the same time some plan for carrying off the superabundant moisture must be in force. Let him learn at once that in Egyptian agriculture there are no underground tiled drains in use; but open ones are formed upon land that requires improving, such as the rice fields and those which, when cultivation has commenced, are found to be impregnated with salts, while a great deal is done by the Government, under whose direction large main cuts are dug to drain off the water on low-lying lands.

On the rich soils water may be lying to a depth of four inches after a flood, but it is so readily absorbed that in six hours none will be left on the Surface; but infiltration from irrigation canals sometimes damages the crops alongside, and in such a case as that a small catch drain will prevent further mischief.

With regard to irrigation, two systems are carried out, the one peculiar to Lower Egypt, the other being utilised in Upper. In Lower Egypt the canal is used for the supply of water to the crops. In Upper Egypt the manner adopted is technically termed the "basin system."

In this latter method embankments are formed to enclose tracts of land well within reach of the Nile flood, which may contain from two thousand to forty thousand acres, according to the means of, or facilities offered to, the agriculturist. Afterwards the proceedings are exceedingly simple. When the inundation is at its greatest height, openings are made and the water is allowed to flow from the river till the sandy surface is covered to a depth of six feet. Then the matter, suspended in the muddy waters, is slowly deposited and goes on sinking till November, when openings are made into canals, and the water is allowed to slowly drain off and make its way back into the river, when the surface of glistening mud that is left is considered ripe for cultivation, and according to the season may measure perhaps four inches in depth.

As soon as the water is gone, the farming operations begin, and in the simplest and probably the oldest form. There is nothing more to be done in these cases, no ploughing or harrowing; but wheat, barley, beans, clover, linseed, and lentils are sown broadcast by the patient labourers, the sowers often sinking knee deep in the mud as they slowly plod or almost wade to and fro. The next proceeding is the burying of the seed, which is generally effected by drawing a large beam of timber over the muddy surface, though at times, when the consistency is greater, the seed is covered in by hand-hoeing. That is all, and the agriculturist leaves the rest for the time being to the efforts of the sun. Germination soon begins, and rapid growth succeeds in the moist mud; while these crops do not need or receive any further irrigation except from rain, which may fall two or three times in the course of growth.

But there are times when no rain at all will come to help the crops, which, however, seem to suffer very little, from the simple fact that the thorough saturation of the subsoil by the flood, and the constant gentle evaporation going on, make up to a certain extent for the want of genial showers, and the failure seems to be confined to the straw alone, which is shorter than if its growth had been influenced by the dropping clouds.

The floods of European lands are, of course, only occasional, accidents due to a prevalence of storm waters, which the regular rivers and the artificial drainage of the country have not power to carry off; while generally they last but a short time, and instead of being beneficial are destructive. The Nile flow is in every respect the reverse. Instead of being occasional and of short duration, it is a part of Nature's routine, and perfectly wondrous in its regularity; while in place of being temporary, as in the floods of our own islands, we have here a lasting overflow.

Again, a flood in the British Islands, where the rivers burst their banks and spread over meadow-land and arable fields, leaves the soil soured, sodden, and obnoxious to the plants which are still alive, whole crops and plantations being often swept away, while those that remain are on the high road to perishing from rottenness.

In Egypt the subsoil of sand is ready to absorb, and the ardent sun to rapidly dry, the surface of the mud as soon as the flood sinks, after its stay of months; while the rapidity of growth soon makes up for the, so to speak, dormant state of the cultivated ground that has been flooded, and, as aforesaid, the water departs, leaving its fertilising riches behind. Then, as stated, follows without further tilling the sowing of the crops, which result in abundant growth. This annual regularity is only

27

marred by the extent of the inundation, which is calculated and divided by the Egyptians into high flood, mean flood, and poor flood, according to how far the waters extend when they leave their natural bed.

It is calculated that in the first case, when the Nile has reached its highest point, it has risen to thirty-three feet; in the second case, the mean flood, thirty feet; and in the third, or poor flood, twenty-three feet above its bed. As a matter of course, the higher the flood the wider spread is the inundation, and the deeper the deposit of fertile mud left upon the land when the river has returned to its ordinary limits.

Stay-at-home people are accustomed to look upon Holland as the land of canals, and the face of this carefully cultivated country is monumental as a specimen of a nation's industry in cutting waterways for the double purpose of draining and traffic, while its drains are as admirable as they are great. Wide tracts of land have been turned from sandy wastes and swamps into fertile meadows and carefully cultivated fields by the Dutch engineers, who have also left traces of their handiwork upon the east coast of England in the drainage of the fens.

But, leaving the supposed canals of the planet Mars to the imaginations of astronomers, it is safe to say that Egypt bears off the palm for works of this description. The ancients knew of their value, and enormous cuts were made by the help of slave labour, and were left to survive the rolling away of centuries, and where not duly cared for, and filled up by the drifting sand, have lain ready to be cleared out, deepened and brought into use again. These have been added to, till at the present time it can be said that the system of canals connected with the main river for the purposes of portage and for perennial irrigation cannot be equalled anywhere in the world.

The barrage of the Delta is of incalculable value, since by closing the sluices the head of water is raised and irrigation made more easy, while the works of this description lately carried out upon the Nile at Assiout and Assouan conserve immense bodies of water, which have formerly flowed regularly down to the sea, carrying with them millions of tons of fertilising mud or warp, with the equatorial washings of the rich, untrodden land. This solution of plant-making soil has gone on downward towards the sea from untold ages, forming by degrees the vast Delta, beside that which was lost to the service of man, merely choking up and making shallow the many watercourses into which the Nile waters have been broken up, and altering the positions of ancient ports and maritime cities now distant from the sea.

Chapter Six.

A good old English gardener once said, "You can't grow things well without plenty of manure," and this the Egyptians found out years ago. They have the great advantage of the fertile mud deposited by the river, but to bring it to its highest state of production land seems to ask for the crude form of animal plant food as well as the vegetable and mineral.

It is to be presumed that there must be a great deal of vegetable fertilisation swept down by the Nile in a decayed state from the forests and swamps of Central Africa, but Egypt itself is no land of forests and that wondrous help to vegetation, leaf mould, may be said to be entirely absent, while the ordinary animal excreta so carefully collected in most civilised countries for application to the land is sadly wanted and neglected here for farm and garden purposes. It is carefully collected, it is true, and dried; but here, in a country where wood is exceedingly scarce, it is used for fuel.

FUEL COLLECTORS.

As a rule, the resulting ashes are regarded as of little worth, whereas they contain, in a mineral form, so many of the constituents of vegetable life that, if preserved, they would be most valuable. In fact, the fellaheen look upon the ashes in the same light as they are regarded here in England, if they are thought of at all, as a coarse ingredient to mix with a clayey soil to lighten it in the place of sand. But in these islands there is the excuse that for the most part they are coal ashes and wanting in fertilising powers. Where they are wood or vegetable ashes the English cultivator has long known their value from the extent to which they are impregnated with potash. Still, there can be no doubt that the ash of the Egyptian fuel, though not returned to the earth in a well-thought-out and business-like way, does play its part to some extent in restoring exhausted soil.

The term "farmyard manure" is common of application, but an English farmer would look at it in amazement and not know his good old friend again, for the Egyptian farmyard manure seems to have been invented by the sanitarians of our dry earth system, being composed of desiccated Nile mud which has been carefully spread over the floors of the cattle-sheds as litter wherever bullocks, cows, horses, sheep, etc., are kept.

In this fine, dry state, the once mud, now earth, is remarkably absorbent and sweetening; most healthy, too, for the animals, who are not seen here trampling nearly knee deep in the soon-made foetid swamp of a country crew-yard. Moreover the earth is frequently removed—to be kept lying in the manure heap for about a year to mature, when it is considered ready for use, and the cattle enclosures and sheds of a farm are remarkably wholesome and clean.

This dry mud is one great source of plant food for the farm, but it is largely supplemented by what the Egyptians term *coufri*, or *sabbakh*. This is not always available, and depends upon the position of the farm; but there are parts of the Delta where, to all appearance, the tract being reclaimed or taken up for bringing into cultivation is so much level, or nearly level, land, with a mound or slight elevation here and there where the winds have drifted the sand apparently to a considerable depth. Except to the eye of the experienced there is nothing to show that flourishing cities and villages have existed there in the past; but many of these slight elevations are the sites where teeming populations once existed, and all has gone back, with some few exceptions—dust to dust. The exceptions are where the spade of the fellah comes upon the remains of a tomb or priestly edifice, these, as is well-known, being the lasting part of man's work, which are being discovered constantly even now, with their builders', sculptors', and painters' handiwork looking, when the sand has been removed, almost as fresh and uninjured as if they were the traces of two or three generations back instead of having been buried many centuries ago.

These solid remains, or ruins, may be comparatively few; but in all probability have been surrounded by an enormous population, whose houses, originally built of the sun-dried Egyptian brick, have in the course of time gone back, like everything animal that surrounded them, to a rough earth ready for the worker's spade, which digs up from an almost inexhaustible mine—with nothing to tell of the past but a few broken shards—a splendid fertiliser for the farm.

But this *coufri* manure requires discrimination in its use, too strong an application being likely to prove hurtful to a crop, seeing that analysis shows that its plant-feeding qualities are due to the salts it contains— sometimes as much as 12 per cent, of salt, soda, ammonia, saltpetre, phosphates, and the like.

The value to an English farmer of such a mine of artificial chemical manure as this may be conceived, and it would make the eyes brighten of one here who strengthens his land by applications of marl, or else has to content himself with a top dressing of chalk from some pit sunk in a corner of his holding.

Fairly plentiful still in Egypt, there must, of course, be a limit to this supply. The taking up of land is going steadily on, and consequently the remains of city after city have been and are being rapidly used up, thus necessitating the establishment of plans upon a practical basis for the restoration of land which should not be exhausted by heavy crops without the cultivator making a proper return. One of our students of agriculture, in a public address, deals largely with the necessity for the dissemination of a practical knowledge of the needs of the land. He speaks of the great waste of fertilising matter in the way in which the refuse stalks of two of the greatest crops of the Delta—cotton and sugar-cane—are burned in the furnaces of engines, for which purpose they are most valuable when it is taken into consideration that fuel wood is a rarity and coal a luxury of exorbitant price.

But after burning, so ignorant have the people been, that the tons upon tons in the aggregate of this rich ash from the engine fires which consume the refuse of the enormous crops of sugar-cane annually grown, have been looked upon as comparatively valueless, in spite of the fact that the ash contains almost all that is required for the growth of so exhaustive a crop, and it has been either cast away or sold for a trifle, to be used up in the manufacture of bricks. He adds, in words full of pregnant meaning, that even the fertile alluvium of the Nile Valley cannot long sustain this treatment without exhaustion, in spite of the much that is done by the feeding off and ploughing in of the leguminous crops, which play a great part in giving back what has been taken away.

Farms here, too, are often found with a large dovecote, as alluded to in the description of the Khedive's estates; for the Egyptian cultivator has a fine substitute for the guano of the Peruvian Chincha Islands in that of the pigeons which are kept in flocks for the sake of this strong fertiliser. Undoubtedly they must take severe toll from the crops, whether green or fit for harvesting, though perhaps this is counterbalanced by the fact that the birds must gain a good subsistence upon the grain that would be wasted or go back to the soil, so much being shed at ingathering time in consequence of the heat.

This carefully-saved fertiliser is used by the Egyptian for applying to vegetables and such productions as water melons and other plants of the gourd family, which depend much for their size on stimulation.

The application of special commercial manures to Egyptian crops may be said to be still in the experimental stage. On the richest and most fertile soils they are not required, but on the poorer soils their effect is very apparent. For the cotton crop, superphosphate and nitrate of soda, in the proportion of 3 to 4 hundredweights superphosphate to 1.25 hundredweight nitrate of soda, mixed and applied to an acre, give a profitable return in an increased yield of cotton. Other manures, such as potash, have been tried, but did not prove satisfactory. Sulphate of ammonia and nitrate of soda give good results on poor land if applied to the wheat crop. As not more than half enough farmyard manure can be produced on large estates for fertilising the various crops, attention will be turned to chemicals should they prove to be profitable after exhaustive experiments.

Chapter Seven.

After what has been written about the water navigation of this country, a few words may be said respecting the means of conducting the land traffic. In the past the great river and its Delta mouths, supplemented by the canals, formed the main roads for the conveyance of produce. Now the iron track has begun to make its way, and the long creeping trains of trucks and carriages may be seen gliding over the plain, drawn by the mighty power of old George Stephenson's invention, though in this hot country the familiar trail of soft whitish grey vapour is often wanting, dying out at once as it does in the rays of the ardent sun. In addition, Egypt is being treated as Britain was some two thousand years ago by the Romans, who well grasped the value of a good trunk road, and while those were formed for military purposes and the holding in check of the subject race, these in connection with the Khedive's peaceful rule and for the advance of agriculture are devoted to the carrying of produce from market to market, or to some railway station, and this, too, at much less cost than in the olden days, when most of the grain was borne from the place of its growth upon camel back, or slung in bags on either side of the patient, vigorous, and handsome donkeys which are raised in this country.

A correspondent of the *Morning Post* writes:

> While Upper Egypt is nowhere more than a fertile strip, bordered by two deserts, the comparatively large area of the Delta, its intersection by a multitude of canals, and the absence of a large system of metalled roads, have long rendered necessary an improvement of communications in the interest both of the fellaheen and of the European or Levantine landowners. Agricultural roads offer but a partial solution of the difficulties caused by these conditions; donkeys, mules, and camels are still highly useful, and will long be extensively used for the transport of commodities over a short distance, or in cases where time is no object to the transporter; but it is unnecessary to dilate on the defects of animal compared with mechanical transport. Branches of the Nile and the canals which in the maps cover the Delta with such a network of blue lines are also of great value, but the number of canals which are perennially navigable is limited, and the canal barge is nowhere renowned for speed, while sailing boats cannot use certain canals at all in the dry season, and their use of others is often attended by the risk of grounding.

En passant, Mr Wallace mentions a singular fact in connection with the making of the trunk roads. In Europe we are accustomed to see them kept as level as is consistent with the cost of making, and raised above the level while provided with proper drains to carry off the too abundant water. Here it has been found that to give the road much rise above the surrounding levels is a mistake, in consequence of the large amount of salt the unredeemed districts contain. The salt rises to the surface, forming an efflorescence as in the American plains, and especially in the stiff lands it has a tendency to interfere with the ways of nature, where the particles adhere together, causing them to fall apart in the shape of dust, which is one of the objectionable features of an Egyptian road.

Anyone who has read about Egypt will recall matters full of suggestion of likely difficulties regarding the keeping open of a road, while those who have travelled through the country have much to say about the prevalence of dust. How many discoveries in the past have been made of wondrous relics that have lain buried for ages covered in deeply—and preserved—by the drifting dust or sand! And, with regard to this drifting, attention has been drawn by Mr Wallace, in his agricultural address, to a singular physical fact in connection with the shifting of the sand. This might be expected to follow, on the whole, the course of the prevailing winds, and be carried mainly in their direction; but there are singular variations, probably due to local waves or currents of air near the surface of the earth.

In one considerable portion of the land of Goshen the sand is swept from south to north, while in another part, along the west bank of the Nile, at the north of Cairo, its direction is from east to west. But a great deal of the raising and drifting of the finer portions of the earth is dependent upon whether the wind be moisture-laden or the reverse. If the air be moist, a breeze blowing at the rate of, say, four miles an hour from the north will have no effect upon the deep dust, while one from the arid south, possessed of about half the other's force, will raise the almost impalpable soil in clouds.

But, as elsewhere, now that Egypt is awakening from her long slumber, the sand is giving way to the soil.

The correspondent of the *Morning Post* gives some very terse and exhaustive accounts of the railway system now extending through the Delta, and dwells upon the fact that the agricultural light railways—similar to the one mentioned earlier in these pages, made by the Khedive to his estates near Cairo—have been a distinct success, and he goes on to say that:

> The broad-gauge State railways of the Egyptian Delta may be roughly compared with the sticks of a fan. Converging at Cairo, the headquarters of the railway administration, and the goal of the provincial lines, the railways diverge to Alexandria, to Dessouk in the north of the Delta, on the Rosetta branch of the Nile, to Damietta, to Salahieh in the north-east, and to Ismailia. Several lines link the important towns on these branches; for example, Mansourah is connected with the Salahieh line, and a railway along the coast connects Alexandria and Rosetta; but large areas, notably in the crowded Menoufieh Province, in Beherah, and in the north-east of the Delta, lacked facilities for rapid transmission

of goods and passengers to the larger towns served by the State lines until the advent of the agricultural railways. It would be unnecessary and unprofitable to enumerate all the agricultural lines which have been constructed in the last few years. Their distribution may be understood if, returning to the fan metaphor, they are regarded as threads running between and generally connecting the diverging sticks of the fan of State lines.

So successful have these lines been that applications have been made for permission regarding the construction of fresh railways to extend in various directions for over another three hundred miles, most of these being in the Menoufieh Province, where desert land is being reclaimed. Mr Gunn's report gives the mileage covered since 1896, when the concessions were granted:

In 1897 there were fifty-four miles of railway open, in 1899 430 miles, and in 1902 673. Within a year or two there will be at least one thousand miles open for traffic.

And, by the way, one of the principal uses made of these lines of rails is for the conveyance of the ancient deposits of *sabbakh* or *coufri* from district to district—the rich fertiliser to the comparatively barren lands— the old-world traces of civilisation to the new, to parts of Egypt which have been written down for ages as desert, but which are now found to become great suppliers of produce that can be easily consigned to the many markets opening up at home and abroad.

Chapter Eight.

Without doubt the Delta is a splendid region for settlement for any young agriculturist who possesses health, energy, and a natural tendency towards those industrious habits peculiar to the successful men of our country, who have always been willing to metaphorically and really take off their coats and do whatever is necessary by way of example. To succeed in Egypt we must take it for granted that he possesses moderate means, or, say, very moderate means, just sufficient to make a small commencement by hiring; or, far better, by the purchase of land, which can now safely be done with good legal security and at a price that before long will in all probability bound upwards to double or even quadruple its present figure. But the thoroughly good sterling advice of the authority already quoted— advice similar in nature has often been before given to intending settlers in Australia—is that a year at least should first be spent in gaining a knowledge of the country, while learning a sufficiency of the common language to enable a man to direct the labourers who will be under him in their field work. And, what is of equal importance, the intending settler, however great may have been his experience, should be ready to cast aside prejudice in favour of his own preconceived opinions, and studiously take note of why this or that course is followed out by old cultivators; he must learn that amidst a great deal of chaff that he may cast aside there are many grains of good sound wheat—otherwise, excellent dearly bought bits of experience. *Festina lente* is a grand old Roman proverb, and the newcomer to Egypt will gain in the end by not being in too great a hurry to start.

Unlike the British farmer, the agriculturist in Egypt has at hand an abundant supply of labour. Housed in the mud huts or sun-dried brick houses adjoining the estates, the labourer is at all hours ready to respond to the demand. He receives one or two acres of land let at a reduced rental; he is a day labourer only, and can absent himself at pleasure to attend to his craft. His wage varies from sixpence to tenpence per day of ten hours in summer and eight hours in winter. He provides his own food.

In disposition this peasant is contented, good-natured, not resentful, and of good physique. He is also very untruthful, unreliable at his work, lazy, cunning, and unconscionable as to the quality and quantity of the task he is put to—in short, a thorough eye-servant. He requires constant supervision, when he will do good work under a trying sun. He promises fair, but performs badly. If he commits a fault and is questioned as to how it happened, one can invariably depend upon his telling an untruth. When working on his own plot he is most diligent, but his methods are not always the best, and he does not get the full benefit from the soil, owing to want of intelligence as to the rules of good husbandry. On a large estate, should extra hands be wanted for a special occasion, a hundred to two hundred men can be had on one night's notice being given—a delightful state of affairs in cases of emergency, though here the farmer does not often suffer from his hay or corn crops being unharvested through the redundance of rain.

A large percentage of the fellaheen are perfectly illiterate, which accounts for their want of readiness to take up the initiative. They have no thirst for knowledge and love in agricultural matters to keep running in the old rut. Exactness, tidiness, and pride in his work are qualities very rarely found in a fellah. Slovenliness in the performance of duties is characteristic of the paid day labourer, and to a lesser degree when working on his own account. In Britain, for instance, where do we find the breeder of stock who excels his neighbours except in the shrewd farmer who, at great trouble and study, and by patient experimenting, attains to success? Not only so, but he is like the leaven which leaveneth the whole lump by raising the standard of a district. The apathy of the fellah is shown in the lack of breeding in horses, cattle, and sheep in Egypt, which is due to want of selecting suitable sires, care in rearing, and the like.

HAND IRRIGATION.

The soil responds to thorough tillage in a marked degree, but too little care is bestowed upon this question of cultivation, as the fellah is prone to scamp his work and leave part of his land solid—that is, not thoroughly stirred. When exposed to the sun the soil cracks and opens into fissures, sometimes as wide as five inches. The fellah is often, too, careless in providing a good bed for the seed, and irregular germination is the result. If the land is judiciously watered and timeously ploughed in a friable condition, it can be brought to a fine tilth without much extra trouble. As it is all soil—nothing in the shape of a bad subsoil exists, as in some parts of Great Britain—deep cultivation is thoroughly beneficial, bringing, as it does, unexhausted soil to the top. Generally in the preparation of the land for the cotton crop, with its deep-searching roots, a depth of twelve inches is attained.

Doubtless much of the apathy of the labouring man amongst the fellaheen is due, as in the case of the rice-feeding Hindoo, to his being to so great an extent a vegetarian. With him the staff of life consists principally of an exceedingly hard kind of bread, baked almost to biscuit, and composed of maize, or dourra, the small-grained millet; and the result of the fellaheen housewife's efforts in this kind of food preparation necessitates dipping or soaking in water before the bread can be partaken of at a meal.

But in such a splendid garden land as Egypt, where cultivated produce attains maturity at so rapid a rate, and where with careful management and such a spring and summer-like climate two or even three crops of vegetables can be obtained in a year, it may easily be supposed that the peasant can provide himself with a constant supply of green food; and he certainly takes advantage of his position, indulging freely in the ordinary vegetables common in the gardens of the West, and supplementing them with the delicious green maize so popular with the American people.

This latter grain is one of the staple foods, when it has come to maturity, of the inhabitants of the Delta. It is ground into a coarse flour, and mingled with a small proportion of barley; while in addition, to give flavour and a slight stimulus to the digestive organs which are brought to bear upon one of the hardest grains in assimilation, a small portion of the peculiar clover-like, many-seeded plant, fenugreek, is added.

FELLAHEEN WOMEN AND CHILD.

Maize gives place to a great extent in Upper Egypt to millet or dourra amongst the poorer orders; but the better-class work-people, who earn much higher wages than the agricultural labourer, are now taking to the general use of wheaten bread.

Although the ordinary fellah partakes of so simple a diet, and may be wanting in energy, loving as he does to glide through life in the same old groove that was formed by his forefathers, he is a well-built, healthy, muscular individual, and is not to be beaten by any coolie as a worker under a torrid sun. Much of his work consists of raising water for irrigation, and if statistics could be produced as to the number of gallons that he sends trickling amongst the roots of the crop, or moistening the land previously in their preparation, ordinary figures would almost fail. Suffice it to say that it is immense. Even now he clings often of necessity to the old, old shadoof—that which is represented in the engraving—which, in spite of its Egyptian name, is

41

only our old friend of the suburban brickfield, a long pole balanced upon a post in scale beam fashion, with a bucket at one end of the pole, a weight at the other, equal to that of the water which is raised from somewhere below for pouring into a receptacle, ready to be dipped again, perhaps, and sent higher by means of another shadoof farther up.

The worker of this primitive water distributer, in his cotton robe, is one of the commonest objects seen upon the banks. The photograph well depicts the sturdy fellah at his task. In addition, there is the old-world sakieh, a much more complicated affair; for here, in the past, primitive ingenuity turned its hand to mechanical construction, and produced after much toil the manual labour-saving and ox- or buffalo-enlisting water-wheel, working after the fashion of one of our river dredges, but clumsy of the clumsy, and having, in place of the metal scoops, so many earthenware pots, held in their places to the periphery of the water-wheel by as many cords, as will be seen in the engraving. Still, it is effective in its way, and the yoked oxen which supply the motive power that turns the heavy wheels raise vast quantities of water year after year. The sakieh is quaint, old-world, and picturesque, and it has served its purpose so well, for who can say how far back in the past, that it never seems to have occurred to the lower order of Egyptian mind that any improvement could be made. That has been left to the West, and now that under the present progressive forward movement of Egyptian agriculture European, and especially British, water-raising and distributing machines are being utilised, the fate of the sakieh seems to be that sooner or later it will merely live to be spoken of as a curiosity, only seen in some artist's representation of the past.

The fellah's habitation has not varied with the years; as in antiquity, so now. The primitive clay hut is simplicity itself. As it is figured in the quaint tomb pictures, so it is to-day in the suburbs and villages—its furniture a wooden chest or two, its cooking utensils a few earthen pots. But his hut is principally his sleeping place, for his life is pretty well passed beneath the broad canopy of heaven. He rises with the dawn to begin his day's work at the plough, or to handle his heavy hoe. At another time the demands of the crops for water or for the mud-laden fertilising contents of the great stream, take him to the shadoof or to guide the bullock or buffalo turning the water-wheel.

As elsewhere, the fellah's wife is the soul of his humble home. She toils busily and patiently through the duties of her little domestic centre, cares for her elders, cooks, and finds time to feed the cattle and collect the sun-dried fuel from off the parched soil, to come back marching homeward, strong and statuesque, bearing the piled-up basket upon her head; while it is she who, while her lord is busily lowering and raising the shadoof, descends knee deep into the river or canal to fill the great, heavy, amphora-like earthen pot and then bear it back to her home, classically picturesque in her drapery as she balances the clumsy vessel upon shoulder or head, and bears the life-giving fluid onward with a steady, easy swing. It is she who makes the dourra, or maize bread, and shapes and stitches the cotton clothing, which is the

43

only wear of all her circle. Unlike her sister of the city, she does not shrink so much from the gaze of the other sex, but still to some extent keeps up the tradition; though wearing no veil she will hold up a portion of her drapery at the coming of the passer-by, or perhaps only place her hand before her mouth.

Woman-like, in spite of her menial toil, she believes in personal care, and her long black hair is carefully dressed and glistens with Palma Christi oil. She paints, too, as of old, the marks appearing upon her chin and forehead, while a string of attractive glass beads decorates and hangs suspended from her neck.

The olden Egyptian costume is that principally affected by the fellah. It consists of a closely-fitting cap of felt or cotton and a long robe of the latter material, deeply dyed of an indigo blue. Shirt and drawers are of the same material, while in some cases a young buck amongst his people will adorn himself, like Joseph of old, in a vest of many colours, borrowed from the Arab, the Persian, or the Turk. As above intimated, the fellah believes in a life of leisure, and finds it rather difficult to make the first start at his daily toil.

AN IMPROVISED VEIL

In the olden days the lot of the fellah was not quite so happy as it might have been. He suffered from enforced labour, and does not seem to have had much chance of appeal. But he had one notable thing in his favour, for a river when in flood is subject to having huge

44

portions of its banks undermined and swept away in a state of muddy solution; and, as was frequently the case, the peasant cultivator, who for the sake of the irrigation had his holding as near the bank as he could contrive to get, was often a great sufferer, being in the possession before the flood of a considerable strip of cultivated land, while after the inundation it was a minus quantity, leaving him to begin life again. Here, however, the law of the land was very equitable upon his behalf, giving him liberty to go either up or down stream to select an equal quantity of the land he had lost that was new and unappropriated, and no one said him nay.

And now, thanks to the just and easy state of the Government, the native working Egyptian is far better off with regard to his condition than he appears to have been at any time in the past. Prosperity surrounds him, and the lesser holders of land, say of from four to ten feddans or acres, rapidly grow well-to-do and distance the larger proprietors. The extent now of the land under cultivation is vastly in excess of what it was. The people are growing more energetic—those of the better class—and are learning fast, while the spirit of emulation is increasing amongst them as they waken up to what modern civilisation will achieve. Their Government, too, is working hard on their behalf, a college having been established at Ghizeh for the purpose of instructing the sons of native landowners and of the working fellaheen class in more advanced agriculture, fitting them in the knowledge necessary for the prosecution of agriculture according to the best forms, the proper rotations of crops, selections of fertilisers, natural and chemical, and, above all, stockbreeding and all that has been learned of late in connection with the dairy.

In brief, much as has been said of the Egypt of the past being the garden of the world, it bids fair to become in the future so great a contrast that old Egypt will pale into insignificance in the bright light of the new.

Chapter Nine.

Horses.—There are no heavy horses used here, such as the Shire or Clydesdale, as the ploughing is done by oxen. The Arab horses—or they might be classed as ponies—measure from fourteen to fourteen and a half hands high. They are not of great substance, but light in the bone, leggy, narrow-chested, though sure-footed and hardy.

Horse breeding is not attended with much success, as regards the production of high-class stock, and re-mounts for the Army and Police have to be purchased in Syria. The stories one reads while at school about the Arab and his steed receive a rude shock when one witnesses the unmerciful way in which the Arab overloads and whips his horses. They are not true horsemen, a fact which is apparent in their methods of training horses to harness.

The Government has supplied stud horses to various districts to try and improve the breed. On the farm horses are used for carting, etc. They are fed on barley and broken straw (*tibn*), the former a bad form of provender for the horse, unless its harshness be ameliorated by crushing.

Cattle.—The work-bullocks are strong, docile animals, and do the ploughing, threshing, raising water, etc. One pair is yoked to a plough. Four pairs are sufficient to work a farm of one hundred acres. Their daily feed is nine pounds of beans and twenty-five pounds of straw. The beans are split, and are eaten uncooked.

Most estates have to purchase their oxen, as very few cows are kept for breeding purposes. The fellaheen keep one or two, and rear the young bulls. Where the soil is richest the cattle are best. In summer the fellah allows his young stock to get into poor condition, and this has an effect on their growth. He has—amongst many other things—still to learn about early maturity. Within recent years work-bullocks have risen enormously in price, owing to more butcher's meat being consumed by the fellaheen and the European visitors. The price of a pair of good bullocks is 45 pounds at the age of four years. These cattle resemble those of the Channel Islands, but are larger. They are very often deficient in depth of rib and chest measurement, hollow-backed, and narrow across the loins, as well as leggy, and they show want of strength of forearm. These are some of the defects which may be eradicated by care in selecting, mating, etc.

THE   BUFFALO   BULL.

47

CROSS-BRED BULL.

Cows are kept and bred from by the fellaheen, who rear the young bulls, while, as we have seen, the cows are used for ploughing. They are not a breed of deep milkers, but the milk is rich in butter fat, 5 per cent, being common; and sixteen pounds of milk will give two pounds of cream, or one pound of butter, which is in demand at from 1 shilling 6 pence to 2 shillings per pound.

Crossing with European bulls has been tried lately, with a measure of success. Some idea of the characters of these animals may be gathered by comparing the illustrations representing both buffalo and ordinary bull with the experimental cross-bred animals reared upon the Khedivial farms. It has been found that crosses between Fribourg bulls (Swiss) and native cows improve the milking qualities and also produce an animal with better points of breeding, without diminishing the usefulness for draught purposes. Fine specimens are to be seen at the present time upon the Khedive's farms. A practice common to the country is that when the cow is milked her calf is tied up beside her and allowed afterwards to partake of its share. If this rule be not observed, the cow will not give up her milk.

Buffaloes.—Large specimens of these peculiar and useful animals have been bred upon the Khedive's stock farm, great enterprise having been exercised for the purposes of improvement both as draught animals and for dairy purposes. One of the sires is a magnificent bull lately brought by his Highness's orders from the Soudan. Both bulls and cows are yoked for farm labour in the fields, while the latter, as dairy stock, are in great favour, their milk being richer in butter-producing qualities than that of the ordinary dairy cow of Europe. Eleven pounds of buffalo milk will churn one pound of butter, but the quality is not so good, being pale in colour, and oily. The yield of milk per twenty-four hours is about thirty pounds.

Donkeys.—Unlike the despised donkey of England, the ass of Egypt is one of the most useful of animals. It is a hardy, patient burden-bearer, but very often ill-treated, notwithstanding its good services. It is employed on the farm for carrying manure in bags slung across the back, and is largely used for the saddle. A well-bred, generously treated donkey is often of a goodly size.

EGYPTIAN SHEEP.

49

Mules.—These are employed for carting, raising water, and other farm work. They are very strong and useful.

Sheep.—Egypt is not a pastoral country, and but scant attention is paid to these animals. They are considered a sort of by-product. When attention is paid to them, however, they yield excellent profit. The ram lambs at five months sell at from sixteen to twenty shillings. No care is bestowed on selection, and breeding from "weedy" rams renders the stock deficient in quality. The duties of the shepherd are light, as the flock is always under his eye at pastures. A very good idea of the Egyptian sheep can be gathered from the illustration.

But the time is rapidly approaching when all this may be changed; for sheep-farming may be looked upon from its double advantage of their increasing popularity for food purposes and their value for the extension of a system of animal manuring, and thus supplying, by feeding off crops, one of the great wants of the country. To a great extent the poor class Egyptian has been a vegetarian, but, with the increase of riches and prosperity in the country, Mr Wallace in his address speaks of the growing demand for animal food, especially mutton; while he reminds his listeners that one of the ways in which an Arab honours his guest is by furnishing his feast with a whole roast lamb.

The Prophet Mohammed, in his sanitary laws to his followers, teaches them to partake of mutton, in his wisdom and knowledge of its superiority to the flesh of the ox, which is considered unclean, pointing to the fact that even in his day cattle were known to be affected with some form of tuberculosis, which might possibly be eaten and thus imparted to the unfortunate partaker of the unwholesome food.

A special choice of site for sheep-farming is necessary, as a matter of course; but portions of the country may easily be selected where they can be kept with advantage—in the Nubarea, for instance. For not only is the land itself undergoing change in its nature, but politically as well. Under the present form of government and the protection to the cultivator which has been the natural result, the farmer is becoming freed from the risks of the past; for, unfortunately, in consequence of a certain inborn notion that has existed among the native Egyptian that everything he covets may be annexed, it has been found absolutely necessary by the grower of sheep to keep an exceedingly sharp eye over his tempting flocks, which have had to be dealt with as if they were in an enemy's land. Driven into folds at night, this has not been sufficient; for as there is a want here of that breed of savage dogs fostered for their protection by the Albanian shepherds, the Egyptian shepherd has to be supplemented by watchmen ready to stand sentry over the flocks by night.

Sheep feeding progresses well during the time of the growing crops; but as these pass away, that form of farming and feeding which may be looked upon as quite modern in its application has proved most advantageous to the keeper of sheep: we mean the plan which agitated the public mind to so great an extent a decade or two back—ensilage—when our country rang with reports of experimental building of costly silos, or the sinking in suitable places of cement-lined tanks in which the newly-cut crops of green cattle food were piled or stacked, rammed down for preservation, and made into what one facetious writer stigmatised as "cattle jam." The idea of the inexperienced was that this treatment of the green grass or clover would result either in rotting or fermentation, with spontaneous combustion to follow, as in the case of a too hurriedly made hay or corn rick in a moist harvest time. But the operations of Nature are as wondrous as they are puzzling, and it was found in our own country that the crop preserved in its silo could be kept for a reasonable length of time, and then cut out in an appetising state, ready for the cattle in a season of scarcity.

Answering so well in Europe, with its frequent rains and superabundant moisture, it is bound to be successful in comparatively rainless Egypt, where the clover can be cut at the exact necessary period and kept ready for use as required—a fact which is likely to give a great impetus to sheep-raising in such a pastureless country as the Delta.

Chapter Ten.

There is every probability of a small capitalist, one who might begin with almost nothing besides so much land and a sufficiency to tide himself over the first few months, making a fair success by the establishing of a poultry farm. In England we are favoured every year with reports of the trials that have been made in this branch of farming; and as a rule it seems that bad weather, the cold, and the cost of keeping, run away with most of the profits. Indeed, the writer's experience points to the fact that few as yet have made a satisfactory living by keeping fowls in this rainy island, while up to the present day our supplies are kept up by the chickens and eggs taken into market from ordinary farms, or collected by hucksters from the cottages over wide districts.

This applies as much to France as to England, for we are indebted to the former country for millions of the eggs with which the metropolis is supplied.

In Egypt, where there is plenty of room and abundant sunshine, fowls might be much improved by the choice of suitable kinds, while some management would be required as to the means of feeding, though one suggestion may be made that, if adopted, ought to prove of great assistance to the fowl and egg farmer.

There is one peculiarity in the growing of grain in Egypt, and this is noticeable in the harvesting, the heat of the sun being so great that the corn of various kinds ripens with such rapidity that if much of it be not cut down and carried in the comparative coolness of the night much of it is shed in the fields and is wasted. Here is a great opportunity for the poultry farmer, or the farmer who merely keeps a few fowls in connection with his general cultivation; for at such times, in a country where double crops prolong the harvest, great numbers of poultry in kinds would be self-feeding, and far superior in quality to many that are brought into the Cairene and Alexandrian markets.

Still, at the present time the occupation has been much improved, for not only are the native markets supplied, but exportation of eggs is on the increase. Far off as Egypt may be, the metropolis is to some extent supplied with its produce, but to nothing like the extent that should be the case, for the London egg merchants will not buy "mummies," which is the cant term for Egyptian eggs, save for about two months in the year, when the European supplies are scarce.

This fact—one which is well worthy the attention of poultry farming aspirants—is entirely the fault of the Egyptian grower, for the London merchants' complaint is perfectly justifiable. It is this—that the Egyptian eggs are exceedingly small, and so badly packed for transit by those who seem thoroughly ignorant of the proverbial fact that "eggs are eggs," that the breakage is enormous, while the entire loss falls on the agents.

Similar complaints used to be made regarding the eggs imported into Europe from Morocco and Algiers, but here those connected with the trade have woke up to their shortcomings and introduced better fowls —the layers of larger eggs—and have also given greater attention to the packing of this exceedingly brittle merchandise. Hence the result has been most satisfactory, and the trade has rapidly increased. Egypt being, then, in much the same latitude as Morocco and Algiers, there is no reason whatever why the former country should not improve its production of poultry so as to vastly increase the demand by raising the quality of its supplies.

Physiologists seem very much behindhand in accounting for the terrible destruction which comes upon countries from time to time. Africa, the ancient home of plagues, is only now recovering from that frightful devastation which affected grazing animals, the wild as severely as the domesticated. From south to north this great portion of the globe was swept by the Teutonically-named Rinderpest. Cattle of all kinds, and the droves of antelope-like creatures which roamed the wilds, perished almost like vegetation before the hot, sweeping blast of a volcano or forest fire. And, though little known outside, Northern Africa has had a trouble that seems to have been special to domesticated birds, a fact which shows that poultry farming in Egypt is not all *couleur de rose*, and that he who would venture upon such a pursuit enjoys no immunity from risks, but must take his chance with the vegetable and fruit growers who, like those in other countries, have their difficulties to face.

One visitation was productive recently of terrible devastation amongst fowls. This was not the familiar "gapes" of the British poultry-yard, but is described as a kind of cholera, so bad that villages have been losing their entire stock, with the natural consequence that the market prices of poultry and eggs have greatly increased—charges, in fact, having doubled and even trebled. Experiments have been tried in the investigation of the disease and the manner of treating it, but so far the only successful way of dealing with the trouble seems to have been by isolation.

But there appears to be every probability of the disease proving only of a temporary nature, and that the production of poultry will be as easy, simple, and remunerative as of old; for, as may easily be understood, poultry farming is bound to be of vast importance in a hot country. Every traveller recalls what a staple food a so-called chicken is in the West Indies; while in the vast plains of India almost every native cottage has its fowls to meet the demand of an enormous consumption. Of the quality the less said the better. The aim of the possessor of a poultry-yard in Western Europe is to produce a plump, square, so-to-speak, solid fowl, broad and full of breast. The Indian bird seems to have been gifted by Nature—in merciful consideration of its being, like most gallinaceous birds, short and hollow of wing and a bad flier, and also of its having to run for its life to escape immolation and consumption—with an abundance of skinny leg, and it never seems to have occurred to the ryot that he might improve the breed.

Even in civilised Egypt there is much to be done in this direction, and an ample field is open to the poultry farmer to improve the quality of the fowl, with success attending him if he will be content to go watchfully to work and make his experiments upon a sound basis, without being too ready to look with contempt upon the experience-taught native ways.

One thing is worthy of remark for the benefit of the would-be poultry farmer, and that is in connection with the marketing, for it is almost a rule that no one in Egypt buys a dead fowl. In Western Europe, of course, the common practice is to send the fatted chickens for sale plucked and neatly trussed. In Egypt it is different, from the fear lest it should have died from natural causes. The result of this style of vendition is the repellent way in which poultry are hawked about the streets of the town, raising feelings for the need of more prevention-of-cruelty-to-animals establishments, though it would be hard work to interfere with a custom which has a good deal of reason on its side, for, waiving the possibilities of purchasing a bird that may have been killed by accident, or possibly have died from disease, climatic reasons must be taken into consideration. Egypt is at times intensely hot, and, whatever may be the fancies of epicures in connection with game, the gourmet has yet to be found with a preference for having his chickens "high."

NATIVE VILLAGE.

Still, as aforesaid, there is something repellent in the way in which the doomed birds are treated. In England a Prevention officer soon summons the huckster who overcrowds his poultry in a crate and does not supply them with food or water; but in Egypt it is one of the common objects of the streets to see a bunch of fowls tied together by the legs and swinging from the vendor's hand, wearily curving up their necks so as to get their heads in the normal position, while every now and then a case may be found where the seller finds that he requires refreshment and callously throws his load upon the ground, while in Eastern fashion he takes his seat at a *café* to sip his cup and smoke a cigarette.

Chapter Eleven.

In such a climate as has been described Egypt offers every inducement for the planting of fruit trees that are likely to flourish under its ardent sun. Attempts have been made, and with fair success, but the raising of fruit has not reached that state of excellence warranted by fertility and the conditions of the climate. Examination very soon shows the reasons for this lack of prosperity, which is clearly the fault of the Egyptian gardener in his want of system, his easy, careless indifference, and his clinging to the old-fashioned way of planting a fruit tree, namely, placing it in a hole in the ground and leaving it to itself.

The first things that strike observers in visiting Egyptian gardens are the overcrowding of the trees, the neglect of precautions to keep them free from weeds, and in many cases the marked absence of pruning dealt out judiciously by one who knows a fruit tree and its needs— plenty of light and air, the removal of cross growth, and the fostering of bearing wood, here frequently injured by rank growth.

Then, again, the Egyptian gardener is as obstinate and conservative as his prototype in the western counties of England, who leaves his ancient apple-trees of the orchard to grow one into the other and become covered with grey lichen, while he religiously avoids the replacing of old and unprofitable trees by young ones.

The result of experience is—and the knowledge of what the land will do makes it certain—that in the following out of this defective system may be traced the want of quality, flavour, and quantity of some Egyptian fruits.

Of these it must be remembered that the settler and commencer of their cultivation would have to deal with several that are new to him in the way of growing, as well as those of the cooler parts of Europe.

Egypt suggests to the reader the ancient civilisation, with its pyramids, temples, and other monuments of its old-time grandeur, the great river, and, above all, the desert; but to come back from these to the simple and ordinary pursuit of gardening, the settler would be able to surround himself, as in California and Florida, but without the bitter disappointments produced by frosts, with several varieties of the golden apples of the Hesperides—oranges, to wit—the sweet, the bitter, the deeply tinted blood orange, and the mandarin. All of them grow well in Lower Egypt, and produce beautiful and profitable crops of fruit, as may be judged by the following. The sweet and mandarin trees will bear, upon a good average tree, from three hundred to four hundred oranges each—that is to say, good, sweet, juicy fruit, and these will sell readily wholesale at about two shillings per hundred; while, in the way of drawbacks for one who expects to make an income from his sales, it will be found here that, just as at home, the tree that in one season bears an exceptionally heavy crop is rather shy in its production in the next.

The words that follow deserve to be written in italics for the benefit of those who know the ravages and foulness that come upon an orange tree in company with the varieties of scale. There are no insect pests, neither, as has been intimated, are there frosts to destroy the bloom.

À propos of this bloom, there is a practice pursued in Egypt which may seem strange to an English gardener, but which adds largely to the profits of the orange grower, and is doubtless beneficial to the tree, relieving it as it may from the strain of overbearing. When the bitter orange is in full flower the trees are shaken, and more than half of the blossoms are sold for the purpose of distillation. The essence produced is used for mixing with drinking water, or for flavouring beverages, while the price received for the petals is about two-pence-halfpenny per pound.

In addition to the oranges, which are in season from November until March, and keep fruiting in beautiful repetition, lemons of several varieties are grown, and are marketable at the same time of year. These are a most popular fruit among the Egyptians, largely utilised as a kind of seasoning in the preparation of cooked dishes, and also much prized for the making of summer beverages in this hot and thirsty land. These are even better friends to the gardener growing for the market than oranges, for they are sure croppers, and command a good price.

Abundance may be written with regard to summer fruits, the list numbering apricots, pears, plums, peaches, apples, grapes, figs, the custard apple, pomegranate, melon, and banana. Of these, bananas, apricots, pomegranates, and figs may be classed as the most profitable fruits of the summer season. But people accustomed to the English Moorpark and Gros Pêche apricot, which, when well-grown upon a south wall or in an orchard-house, is one rich bag of reddish amber, deliciously flavoured honey-like juice, would be much disappointed in the abundant apricots which are produced upon standard trees for the Egyptian market. They are finely flavoured, but small, hard, and fibrous; and an experienced cultivator of fruit trees states that it is very probable that the deficiency in quality and the reason that so far it has not thrived to perfection is, paradoxical as it may sound, that it matures too quickly, which is another way of saying that the climate is too fine for it. Still, there is every reason to believe that skilful management and choice acclimatisation, or the raising of new sorts, may result in the production of finer apricots than those now grown in England, where in some parts a manifest deterioration has been in progress, so great that growers are destroying their apricots and replacing them with fruit trees more suited to our sunless climate.

Some years back a novelty made its appearance in the Alexandria district. This was a veritable plague of Egypt, though undoubtedly a visitant from abroad. It was a banana disease, which in its inroads played great havoc amongst the plantations. Scientific examination was brought to bear, and the cause was found to be a parasitic nematode which attacked the roots of the plant.

Fortunately the trouble was local, and the infection limited in its area, while at the present time many of the plantations are free from the pest.

With regard to peaches, the way is open to the enterprising and clever cultivator, for with such a constant supply of sunshine much ought to be done in the way of growing this queen of fruits. Many of us here in England, who have to trust to trees laboriously trained against a wall, or spread out and tied in to wires at the cost of many a back and neck ache, beneath the sloping glass of an orchard-house, have read with watering mouths of the standard trees of the United States, where the fallen peaches are gathered up in barrowfuls and considered of no account.

Abundance rules there, and possibly it may be that this is due to the intensely hot summers of the States and their frigidly cold winters; for this seems to be the nature of the climate in the country from which the peach sprang and took its Latin name, *Persica*; for there, following upon the summer heats, winter comes down from the mountains intensely cold.

This balance is wanting in Egypt, where, so far, peaches have not proved to be a success. The trees grow well and bear fruit that is fairly large in size, but does not possess the fine aromatic, juicy flavour of a well-matured English peach grown upon a wall and only protected during the time of frost, those raised under glass, save in size and appearance, never approaching the open-air fruit.

The Egyptian peaches are hard and fibrous, as well as wanting in the piquant bitter almond flavour so much esteemed. Possibly the selection of better kinds may make a great change in the hands of careful cultivators, but in common fairness it is right to say that the successful production of this favourite fruit in Egypt is open to doubt.

So far, too, another stone fruit, the plum, is not extensively grown, while the plums produced in the Egyptian garden cannot compare with those imported from Europe. But this fruit is not such an aristocrat among the luscious beauties of the garden as the exacting peach, and there is nothing to prevent, either in soil or climate, a finer quality being grown in the Delta.

What is needed is the selection of new and suitable varieties, accompanied by careful watching of results; in fact, the intelligent management of a good experimental gardener, not one akin to that of Egypt, who selects with extreme conservatism the easiest way to his desired ends. He consequently devotes his time to those fruits which flourish easily and well. His attention has been given principally to the growing of the *citrus* family, to the exclusion of such fruits as pears and plums, which are imported from Syria and Turkey. In fact, in spite of the possibilities of the Delta, how great is the want of enterprise may readily be seen when it is stated that the value of the imports of fruit may amount to many thousand pounds per annum.

Unfortunately, our two most home-like and familiar fruits—apples and pears—do not succeed here, the climate being far too hot. Pears have a very small share of the land, and the fruit is not of the best quality. But while it is doubtful about the apple, this doubt ought not to extend to the pear, which is a lover of heat, and, as regards the better sorts, delicate and tender in its constitution. There can be no doubt that if a careful selection of some of the best French and Belgian varieties were introduced, a fair meed of success would be the result, for it seems almost contrary to reason that such kinds as the fragrant *Doyenné de Comice* and *Glou Morceau*, which fail as standards in the inclemency of an English season, and crack and speck if they are not protected by a wall, should not succeed in Egypt if they are given a fair trial.

Not that there is much need for experiment in a country which can grow its grapes gloriously in the open air, the vines not asking for the help of glass. Some half dozen varieties are produced in Egypt, and flourish well under treatment of the simplest kind. The cultivation of the vine extends over the whole of the province of Fayoum. In this latter district a white grape, called after its habitat the "Fayoumi," is the favourite in the market, and it is the earliest that ripens. The berries are medium sized, but the flavour is excellent and the fruit very juicy.

There is little question of training or trellis work, for, somewhat after the fashion of the vineyards in France, the vines are grown as bushes of about two feet high; and the result, though not the production of the bunches of the Vale of Eshcol, is still abundance.

Two varieties are grown in the Delta and Cairo districts, namely "Roumy"—a kind derived from Greece—and "Shawishi." Here, as opposed to the cultivation in the province of Fayoum, the vines are mostly trained on lattice work so as to form what the old gardeners called a pergola, or covered way. Both these varieties are heavy croppers, bearing bunches whose berries are of a greenish red, while the flavour is very good.

Egypt is a land of vines and vineyards, much space being given to the cultivation of the grape, though not for the purposes of carting to the winepress, the Moslem religion being antagonistic to the grape's fermented juice. Each district has its favoured kind, and in that of Alexandria and along the shore of the Mediterranean the vine is abundantly grown close to the ground, the soil being pure sand.

There is a peculiarity in the cultivation here, for V-shaped trenches are cut to a depth of from six to nine feet. Then vine shoots are planted in the bottom of the trench, where the young rootlets they put forth are within reach of water. Vegetation is rapid, and the canes gradually cover the slopes on either side, while in two years the vines begin to bear.

The bushes receive no irrigation from above, only depending upon the so-called winter rains, which are fairly frequent near the sea, and, as has been shown, gaining their support from beneath the sand at the bottom of the trench. But though no irrigation is brought to bear, these ground vineries require annually an application of manure if the best results are to be obtained.

As the land of the Delta is practically level, it affords scarcely any opportunities for the growth of the grape vine upon sunny slopes, this being the only instance in Egypt where grapes are grown with this exposure, while these slopes are all artificially made.

As regards insect pests, they may be almost classed as *nil*, and the grower will not hear of thrip and scale, mealie bug, or red spider, so that the cultivation is conducted under the most favourable conditions; but the ubiquitous sparrow is even there, and, unless means are taken to scare away or destroy him, his ravages amongst the sweet berries are great.

Here, too, as may be supposed where grapes are produced to so great an extent, the thinning of the berries is not resorted to, and consequently they are not so large as might be expected from the heat of the climate and the favourable conditions under which they are grown, nor is the flavour so fine as that of the beautiful bunches so carefully tended and watched under glass in an English vinery; but they command a ready sale at about twopence per pound when the fruit is ripe, from the beginning of June.

Chapter Twelve.

That delicious European fruit, the strawberry, by nature a dweller in cool and Alpine regions, was not known in Egypt till within forty years ago. Planted as an experiment by someone familiar with its qualities, it seems to have passed rather an unfavourable time in popular estimation; but it is now gradually gaining in favour, and the area under cultivation is steadily extending.

The fruit is ripe in November, and finds a ready sale at tenpence per pound; while, if the cultivation is good and well-managed, the return to the planter may be reckoned at forty pounds for the produce of an acre.

To an Englishman familiar with the strawberry and its growth, one knowing the botanical character of the plant and the love of its roots for a rich clay land, it seems surprising that it should flourish so well in the sandy soil of Egypt. But, of course, this is explained by the yearly deposit of rich silt, or warp, the result of the annual floods.

Fortunately for the grower, he is not troubled as in England by woodland birds, the Eastern crops suffering very little from their ravages, while the plant enjoys almost an immunity from the attacks of insect plagues.

In the goodly list of luscious fruits we now come to figs—not the overgrown, sickly fruit that only ripens under very favourable circumstances in England, but the rich saccharine bag of embedded seed that we know best in its dried and pressed form as the common fig.

Its cultivation is spread over the whole Delta and the Fayoum, where its milky, succulent stems and dark green leaves flourish thoroughly well. The trees, as a rule, grow to a height of nine or ten feet, are well branched, and find great favour with the native gardener, for they possess the admirable qualities of requiring not much attention, very little manure, and no pruning. Joined to this, the trees are very prolific, and the luscious fruit finds great favour with the people.

Another popular fruit which grows without much attention save irrigating, and that to a very moderate degree, is the prickly pear.

Here in England the melon is looked upon as a delicacy. Gardeners vie one with the other in its production, and seedsmen push forward this fashionable fruit by advertising their own special specimens of prize kinds, and these may be almost classed as legion.

In Egypt the varieties are roughly divided into two, the sweet and the water melon, and they both flourish wonderfully. They are sown in February and March, and thrive best in light loam, while their period of growth extends to about four months.

BALANCES THE CLUMSY VESSEL

In their rapid development they attain to a goodly size. For instance, a water melon may reach the weight of thirty pounds, while from a marketing point of view, taking large and small together, so as to strike an average, the wholesale price may be placed at fivepence per melon, and the cultivator of an acre of land devoted to this produce may reckon on receiving from forty to sixty pounds—pretty satisfactory for the four months of growth and the land ready for planting with some other crop suitable to the season, for the grower has no dreary months of winter to intervene.

The cultivation of the sweet melon is similar to that of its relative, but the fruit is finer in flavour and the plants not so prolific. Consequently the grower's receipts are much smaller, a fair computation of the returns from an acre being from about thirty to forty pounds. There is another disadvantage, too, in the growth of this fruit. It must be consumed within some ten days after being fully ripe, whereas the sturdy water melon will keep good for over a month. In spite of the good qualities of the melon, its ease of growth, and the market requirements, nothing like sufficient are grown, the demand being supplied by the importation of large quantities from neighbouring countries.

This popular fruit is always looked upon as deliciously refreshing and fine in flavour, but it may be mentioned here how much climate has to do with the quality of the fruit. Some years ago a friend, after a prolonged stay in Egypt, presented the writer with a few seeds of the Egyptian melon. These were planted here in England and nursed up under glass with all the care that good gardening and watching could bestow. Everything was done to the exotic plants that a certain amount of experience in growing melons could supply, and a couple of them flourished exceedingly—under glass, be it remembered, in a heated house—blossomed, and bore several fine large green fruit, whose increase was watched and maturing waited for, but in vain.

Presumably there was a certain amount of fragrance and ripening, for the fruit changed colour and gave forth the familiar odour; but the anticipations of enjoying a delicious Egyptian melon were not fulfilled. A good ripe vegetable marrow would have put either of them to the blush.

Pumpkins, big and gourd-like in growth—*pastiches*, as they are commonly called—are most abundant in the early winter months, and are largely brought down the river from Upper Egypt in barges or feluccas with graceful lateen sails. They form a pleasant addition to the food of the poor, while in their growth, favoured as they are by a hot sun, rich soil, and a sufficiency of moisture, their increase is almost fabulous, and anyone of curious taste and plenty of patience, aided by a powerful magnifying glass, might in all probability be gratified by seeing the creeping growth of the watery vine and the steady swelling out of its heavy earth-supported fruit.

Another fruit upon our list is the pomegranate, of late years made familiar upon the barrows in the London streets, and looking when cut open something like an unwholesome blood orange that has aborted and taken to growing an enormous excess of pips embedded in jelly within a hardened peel.

In spite of the enterprise which has brought the fruit here, it seems hardly likely to bring the shippers much reward; but it is extensively grown in Egypt, is in great demand, and very profitable.

To continue with unfamiliar fruits, we may next name the great date palm, which may be looked upon as the most common tree to be found in Egypt, growing as it does all over both the upper and lower regions, as well as on the sandy shores of the Mediterranean Sea. No wonder that it is so largely planted, for its fruit is everywhere consumed by the people as a portion of their food.

The tree begins to bear five years after planting, and should take the record as a profitable friend of man, for under favourable conditions it will go on bearing for a hundred years or more, while a good tree will bear, on an average, over a hundredweight of fruit, which is disposed of amongst the people at the popular price of one penny per pound.

The fruit ripens in September, and where the trees are selected, are of the best variety and well attended to, the profits are very good, especially if they are planted in a garden, where their tuft of leaves, raised high upon their tall, smooth stems, throws so little shade that the ground beneath can be profitably planted with other crops, such as the ordinary domestic vegetables of our own country, haricot beans, peas, spinach, etc.

"The large, dark, red-skinned, hard date," a friend writes from Cairo, "has long been plentiful, and forms one of the staple foods of the populace. But to-day—i.e., mid-October—the soft, small luscious date was served at table. This is a most delicious fruit. It tastes for all the world like caramel toffee, though of course much softer. These dates are wonderfully cheap. They do not, however, keep more than twelve hours after picking, and then begin to ferment and taste like beer. They are most plentiful, and there is, no doubt, much waste. I should think that a strong spirituous liquor could be distilled from them."

Other fruits may be mentioned, such as the quince, loquat, lotus, and that favourite of farther east, the delicious mango; but these are not extensively cultivated, and may very well be excluded from a list of fruits that might be profitably grown for market purposes. The wonder is that the mango has been neglected, comparatively, up to now. Still, the Egyptians are waking up to its value, for during 1903 there has been in Cairo a very plentiful supply of this luscious fruit, which bears some semblance in the eating to a very rich and juicy apricot, resembling it also in colour.

The old saying of the Anglo-Indian who makes it a favourite, in spite of a slight suspicion of turpentine in its flavour, is doubtless well-known to the reader—that which suggests that the best way of combating the superabundant juice and its gushing ways is to sit in one's bath when partaking of the fruit.

In summing up the prospects of fruit growing in Egypt, Mr Wright states that he has no hesitation in saying that the conditions for gardening in Egypt are certainly far more favourable than in such an uncertain climate as that of England, where in one night so much blossom may be destroyed by frost; while in Egypt one never hears of such a thing as a total failure of crop.

Chapter Thirteen.

To take a stride now from the delicious and attractive to the homely and useful, but at the same time more general and profitable growing crops of Egypt, let us turn to the gardener's mainstay—his vegetables.

Here the first thing that strikes a visitor to this semi-tropical land is the familiarity of many of the garden crops—some, to use an old-fashioned term, grown out of knowledge; others perhaps wanting in the qualities of the home country.

Most familiar of all—certainly the most homely and extensively grown, with great profit, is the cabbage, in three varieties—the White Drumhead, the Red Drumhead, and the Savoy. Here a little unfamiliarity steps in, and that is in the usage, for the cabbage in Egypt is utilised by the people as a salad as well as for cooking.

From a gardener's point of view the head is not so large and hard, the vegetable not forming a solid heart as it does in England. But this may be accounted for by want of sufficient manure and attention—good gardening, in short—and perhaps the climate is not wholly to blame.

The cauliflower flourishes fairly well under similar cultivation to the cabbage, but being more delicate requires greater attention; differing from the latter, the heads are well formed, but it is necessary to shade them when coming to perfection, the clean, white growth being liable to be damaged by the too ardent sun.

Good cauliflowers command a ready sale at better prices than are to be had in London as a rule, the average cost being from twopence-halfpenny to fivepence per head.

Another very familiar crop is seen largely in Egypt—the leek. This is a profitable vegetable, which grows to a good size, is easily cultivated, and realises a total per acre of about fifteen pounds. The carrot, too, is largely grown—in two varieties, the native and the Greek. The native kind is sown in September, and is ready for lifting in January; while the Greek variety, sown in the same month, is also used for the production of a summer crop in February. A deep soil is necessary, while its sandy nature in Egypt is most suitable for this root, and when carefully cultivated a fair return may be expected.

One of the most extensively grown vegetables, a very general favourite almost everywhere except in England, is the garlic. It does well in Egypt, often in plots of as much as two acres, and has the advantages of not requiring great care in cultivation, nor much water; while an average crop will yield of the silvery bulbs enough to be valued at about fifteen pounds per acre.

The onion, again, proves itself to be a most thriving inhabitant of this Eastern country, growing hard, firm, clean-skinned, and healthy. In this sunny clime it is extensively grown, and not merely for home use. The kind most popular is the red Spanish onion, and it is cultivated both in Upper Egypt and Lower, there being this peculiarity of difference, namely, that the Spanish onion grows to a larger size in the south, while the flavour of those grown in the Delta is superior.

A few words will not be out of place respecting the cultivation of this vegetable in Upper Egypt, where it is grown most extensively as a farm crop for export. The seed is sown in the month of October, transplantation takes place in March, and, all going well, the crop is ready for lifting in June or July. After the transplanting no irrigation is required. The yield is approximately four to five tons per acre, and the market price two pounds per ton.

The next vegetable on our list when grown in quantity looks wonderfully familiar and home-like. It is the artichoke—not that of tuberous and sunflower-like growth, but the deeply cut, acanthus-like leaved ornamental plant of English gardens, with its majestic thistle-like purple head.

This is one of the best-paying garden crops, these heads being greatly in demand by Europeans, though not much sought after by the natives. In the culture it will be found that the growth is excellent for four years, when transplanting becomes necessary and should be resorted to.

Asparagus is decidedly one of the best-paying crops in Egypt, and naturally always in great demand by the Europeans who visit or pass through the country in ever-increasing numbers. The cultivation is the same good old-fashioned style practised in England, the beds being well prepared and generously treated with stimulants. All that is required to secure a fine crop is proper attention under skilled direction, for there are no drawbacks from frost, the grower never finding the sturdy greenish purple shoots of yesterday drooping over and destroyed by the morning's frost.

Well treated, the beds will remain good for from ten to fifteen years, a very modest computation this, for if well-managed and not cut too hard, a good asparagus plantation ought to remain prosperous for twenty or thirty years. As the result of his generous treatment in the way of stimulants, the grower may expect to receive wholesale from two shillings to five shillings per hundred shoots, according to their size.

That easily-cultivated wholesome vegetable, spinach, is largely grown from September till January; while now may be added, most extensively raised, a vegetable new to Occidental eyes, in company with three more which have long periods of growth, well fitting one to succeed the other.

The first is a small-flowered mallow, whose period is from September to October—it is much relished by the poorer Egyptians as a cooked vegetable resembling spinach; purslane is another very easily-grown plant, whose period is from March to September; Jews' mallow, too, is a vegetable greatly esteemed by the natives. This is cultivated, and also found growing wild in the fields. It is much in demand as a summer vegetable. Okra is another dish held in high estimation; it is not difficult to grow, and forms a good paying crop.

To return to the familiar vegetables of Western gardens, we have a great favourite in the shape of the haricot bean. This grows exceedingly well in Egypt, on condition of its being well supplied with water, while the rapidity of its maturing is marvellous, showing, as it does, the beauty of the Egyptian climate and the power of the sun, for it is fit to pick thirty days after sowing, and the land ready for another crop, a fact which seems almost incredible.

The next on the list of profitable vegetables is the ordinary broad bean, but this is not extensively grown, as it is only consumed by the upper class natives, the poorer people preferring the ordinary horse bean, which is grown as a winter crop. These beans are a very common article of food, and are bought by the peasantry, ready boiled, in most public places. They are also largely employed as provender for the working cattle. The roots of an arum and of the lotus, too, are largely consumed, and no wonder in the case of the latter in such a dreamy land; but the effects are not quite the same as the former Laureate described.

The turnip, so popular in England, finds little favour, though it is easily raised as a medium-paying crop, and, odd as it may sound, it is principally used pickled.

Colocass is generally grown upon the farm. The tubers are large, about the size of an English turnip. This is a splendid paying crop, which is largely consumed as a vegetable and forms one of the staple foods of the fellaheen.

The sweet potato is also a common vegetable here, but the name sounds foreign to an English cultivator. It is a plant with tuberous roots of a white colour, mostly eaten roasted, and, like the colocass, it is a favourite food of the farm labourer. The value of the produce of an acre may be estimated at ten pounds, and the duration of the crop is about four months.

The cucumber thrives very well in Egypt, and, of course, there is no necessity for the protection of glass. It is as popular as in England, but perhaps more utilised, lasting well through summer into autumn, and proves to be a very paying crop, provided it has a plentiful supply of water. This may also be said of the two varieties of vegetable marrow, the green and white, which are largely raised. The fruits are most popular when very young, and are much relished when treated as the cucumber is in England—that is to say, served as a salad, though it is cooked as well. This, like the cucumber, is a medium-paying crop. As for the latter, it has been a favourite object of culture, dating right back to the days of the Israelites. The allusion to the cucumber will be recalled, and all species of this family are cultivated with assiduity. Not that there is anything wonderful in this, for in a hot country fruits and vegetables of rapid growth, and which cause little trouble, are sure to be affected. We say rapid growth advisedly, for in favourable seasons the shoot of a cucumber may be almost seen to grow, achieving as it does, at times, a length of twenty-four inches in a day and night.

The ordinary salads and herbs of the English garden are easily raised, and form profitable crops, available summer and winter, and are highly esteemed. Among other plants we have poppies, madder, indigo, flax and hemp; while in the province of Fayoum one very charming form of gardening is practised, namely the growth of the rose tree, from which is prepared the rose water so popular all through the East.

As for flowers of all descriptions, where they are scarce it is the fault of the people, for many of our most brilliant kinds, especially the more tender, which are raised in our islands only with care, brighten the land and flourish everywhere like weeds.

Our ornamental hothouse growth, the eggplant, here forms a most important vegetable, which is extensively cultivated. It is similar to the aubergine, which is used in France and seen occasionally in Covent Garden Market; but the years glide by, and its bids for popular favour have met with but little success.

It is the reverse in Egypt, where its use is general, whether as a cooked vegetable, pickled, or in its raw state. It demands a rich, deep soil, and is raised in both varieties, white and black, for use in summer and autumn, and proves to be very profitable to the grower.

Chapter Fourteen.

Perhaps the most successful vegetable that has been introduced into England is the tomato. Forty or fifty years ago a punnet or two of the attractive vivid scarlet fruit might be seen in season at Covent Garden Market. They were known as "love-apples," and probably were bought and consumed; but their growth into favour was very slow before becoming a fashion, and, with most people, an acquired taste. The tomato forms a summer production of the English market gardener, who is rivalled by the growers of the Channel Islands; and it is sent into market daily by the ton; while, when the inclemency of our climate renders firing absolutely necessary, the enterprising growers of the Canaries keep up the supply. Flourishing so well just off the west coast of Africa, it is only natural that the tomato should find a congenial home in the fertile East of the great Continent, and it is extensively grown with increasing success in Egypt.

As an example of the tomato being treated as a profitable crop, here is an instance of what has been done in the way of market gardening in the district of Alexandria, and may be done again by those persevering cultivators who are struggling to make a moderate living.

A father and two grown-up sons may rent a plot of land of, say, four acres in extent, the rent of which perhaps reaches ten pounds per annum, the gardener having to raise water for irrigation purposes.

The occupation of the land would commence on the first of August. The soil may be classed as pure sand, which naturally requires a liberal application of farmyard manure. The ordinary tillage having been carried out, the cultivator begins by transplanting seedling tomatoes about the beginning of September. Not being prepared to plant the whole of his four acres with tomatoes, he sows on another part vegetable marrows, which in this hot climate are ready for plucking in six weeks, the plants continuing to bear for a month; while directly this supply is finished another crop of marrows may be sown on the same land.

Meanwhile, the tomatoes are pushing forward to be ready by the first of January at a time when the price is generally good, though probably in no other vegetable is there so great a variance in the amount it will fetch, dependent, of course, on the scarcity or plentifulness of the crop.

It will be news, probably, for the British grower when he reads that the wholesale price of tomatoes in Egypt varies from one farthing to fivepence per pound. Perhaps he may open his eyes a little wider when he reads that a fair estimate of the gross return from growing tomatoes for the market supply of Alexandria will vary from ten pounds to fifty pounds or more per acre; and, of course, this is in the open ground, forming an almost immediate return, and with no preliminary outlay for glass houses.

But there are always drawbacks in gardening; and one of these, which may occasionally mar success, is caused on this land so near the sea by the fogs. These, if they attack this delicate plant, so famous here at home for developing aphides and fungoid diseases, like their unfortunate relatives the potatoes, destroy the leaves, blacken them, hinder the setting of the blossom, and generally reduce the crop.

Several men have been known to engage in this cultivation in the neighbourhood of Alexandria during the last five years, and apparently they have financially improved their position.

Leaving the aristocratic tomato and turning to its poor relative the potato, it might have been hoped that in such a hot, sandy land as Egypt, where thousands of acres offer the same facilities, and are made as rich and fertile as the famous warp-land potato tracts of north Lincolnshire and south Yorkshire, a home would have been found where it would flourish free from disease.

Unfortunately, the information to be given to the horticultural or agricultural grower upon this point is not good; in fact, quite sufficient to make the writer suggest that it should be a crop to be left alone.

Certainly potato growing is tempting; the cultivation is simple, the crops heavy and very profitable *if*—this is a very large "if," and means so much, especially connected with weather and disease. Experience of long years employed in gardening and farming in Egypt suggests that if the cultivation of the potato is entered upon it is best to be grown on the farm or by large market gardeners.

Good quality potatoes, such as are marketed in England, are rarely found in Egypt. The crop is generally grown from "seed" imported from France and Italy, and a sandy soil is chosen. Two crops, however, can be taken from the land per annum. The first is planted in October, and should be ready for lifting in the beginning of February, a period of five months; the second, planted in February, is ready for harvesting in June—the duration of time for the crop to be on the land, one hundred and ten days. It sounds novel to a British grower to speak of a winter and a summer crop of potatoes, two crops in the year; but this is so, and the winter may yield three tons per acre, while the summer produces five to six; while the current price per ton returned to the grower is about seven pounds. As this is the most popular of vegetables, and the demand always so great for good, well-grown new potatoes, experiments have been tried for raising these in the neighbourhood of Cairo and sending them packed in boxes to arrive in England, when they would be eagerly bought up in the market as luxuries, at the beginning of March.

Here are the returns of the experiment. From fifteen to eighteen pounds per ton were realised; carriage, freight, and other expenses amounted to three pounds per ton, leaving a margin of profit over the price in Egypt of from five pounds to eight pounds sterling. Enough this to make the Delta worthy the name of a land of promise, and especially more so when it can be, and is, announced that it is a country where there is no potato disease. In exceptional cases, however, there is the drawback of cold weather, which retards the growth of the winter crop.

Another objection is that all the seed potatoes—and these are heavy of freight—have to be imported, as storing throughout the summer is impracticable.

It is only fair to say, however, on behalf of our good old mealy friend, the familiar object of every man's table, that in his guise of a foreigner —an African—he will be much better if he is let alone and not subjected to the tricks of trade, which recoil upon and tend to spoil his character. For in the harvesting of the crop a bad practice has arisen with the Egyptian market gardener, who generally carries on his operations in the neighbourhood of some irrigation canal connected with the Nile, where he has, so to speak, abundance of conserved water always on tap ready to give his fields a heavy watering. This he bestows upon his potatoes just before turning them out of the ground, as he finds that it greatly increases the weight of the tubers; but it spoils their quality, and makes them what a Londoner calls "waxy," and a north countryman "sad."

One ought not to close one's list of garden or farm productions without adding the names of a few so-called spices, or flavour-producing plants, which are always in steady demand and flourish well in the valley of the Nile. Among these are the capsicum, the green and the red, which are most easy of culture, and come to maturity rapidly with the same treatment as is accorded to the tomato. There is also the lesser kind, or chilli; the caraway famous for its seeds, the coriander, and dill; while as to the familiar mustard, it hardly asks for cultivation at all, but grows rapidly and ripens well, while the seed, when ground into the familiar condiment, is pungent and aromatic in the extreme.

As is well-known, a fine class of tobacco is grown pretty largely in the Delta. It is wanting in the strength of the kinds raised in the West Indies and the United States. It is excelled, too, in potency by the products of the East Indies; but it is of a very delicate flavour and much liked, though not so popular as that of Turkey in Europe and Asia. But this is partially due to want of usage on the part of smokers, who are not accustomed to the pungency and fine aroma which appertain to the Egyptian tobacco as compared with the Turkish. But the North African is remarkably good all the same, and flourishes splendidly, there always being abundance of sunshine at the picking time and excellent opportunity for *haying* the crop. For, after all said and done, a great deal of the aroma of tobacco depends upon the fermenting process it goes through in being dried and pressed, just as a well-made crop of grass, hay, or clover, is dependent upon the skill of the farmer and his choice of weather.

Chapter Fifteen.

Supposing an enterprising personage to have taken up a tract of the desert of, say, one hundred acres in Egypt, where divisions must not be looked for in the way of fence or hedge, but dependence placed upon the irrigating drain, it will be as well to give a list of the farm implements he would require, and their cost—always presuming that he is prepared to be content, certainly at first, with the ordinary contrivances of the country, which are rough, but very cheap.

WRIGHT'S TURN-WREST PLOUGH.

Necessaries are given here, and nothing more; while the accompanying illustrations spread through the text afford a very good idea of the objects that will become familiar upon his pioneer land.

Four native ploughs, exceedingly rough in construction, for tickling the soil that is to laugh with a harvest, their cost about ten shillings each; a baulk wood, to be drawn by oxen, mules, or donkeys, over the yielding surface and act the part of a roller, six shillings; a ridging box, for preparing the land for potatoes or sugar-cane, two shillings; two scrapers, eight shillings; chains, six shillings; one lorry, five pounds; two box carts at four pounds each; two threshing norags at eight pounds each; total, thirty-two pounds ten shillings.

Of course, it is open to the man of enterprise to invest in the different ingenious contrivances of the British agricultural implement maker, such as the admirable invention the Patent Turn-Wrest Plough, invented by Mr Thomas Wright, whose experience in the cultivation of the Khedive's land resulted in his bringing to perfection an implement exactly suited to Egyptian needs.

FELLAHEEN LABOURERS.

The list given above names all that is absolutely necessary in a country where the tiller of the soil is so munificently aided by the almost incessant sunshine and abundant water.

But the farm implement *par excellence* of the fellaheen, the tool which is to him what the shovel is to the British navvy, an instrument with which nearly everything in the way of moving the soil can be done, is the fas, the broad-headed hoe seen carried by the two fellaheen labourers in the engraving accompanying this chapter. It is one of the first inventions of the cultivator, and not so very far removed from its pierced flint representative occasionally turned up amongst the weapons and tools of primitive man; but when bronze, and later on iron, began to yield to the inventor, and the action of fire was utilised by the Tubal Cains of their day, the broad-headed hoe began to develop; and we have it spread, in a very similar form to that still used in Egypt, all round the world where men commenced to till the soil. For we see it to this day very similar in shape in those two vast agricultural countries, India and China, while in Egypt it is handled by the fellaheen labourer in a way which is beyond praise.

NATIVE PLOUGH

The native plough, as seen by the photographic reproduction, is a very primitive implement, the date of whose invention must be sought for by an examination of some of the characteristic gravings in marble to be found in the Egyptian tombs, where the pursuits of the old-time inhabitants are recorded in a style that is absolutely wondrous.

It consists of a pole of wood measuring about ten feet in length, which is strongly bolted to the sole or body of the plough. This soie, which measures three feet, is shod with a share resembling a pointed shovel. The end of the pole is attached by a rope to the yoke, which lies across the necks of the bullocks, buffaloes, or even camels—as seen in the case of the Norag, drawn round and round over the threshing-floor—which are utilised by the Egyptian cultivator according to his means, while the labourer guides the plough by the aid of an upright handle. This implement does not turn over the soil, and may be properly classed as a one-tined cultivator. There is a quaintness and old-world look, as shown in the photographs, in the mixture of forces, a huge buffalo bull being mated with a small native ox, a bullock with some fine-grown ass, while cows are frequently yoked together to help and drag the light plough. Whether horses of the type of our heavy, slow-going farm breed will finally work their way to the front remains to be seen; but at present they have hardly begun to oust the old-world yokes of strangely assorted beasts from the turning up of the soil. It is more probable, unless the fuel difficulty stands in the way, that the larger tracts will be further brought into cultivation by means of steam and the deep subsoil ploughs which do such an immensity of work in a single day.

A BADLY-MATCHED PAIR.

As will be noted in the description, the modern native plough is single stilted, and it might be supposed in a country like this that such an implement had been in use ever since the plough's invention; but as in many other records that have been unearthed, engraven in stone in the wonderful pictorial writings found in temple and tomb, we have proof that this was not always the case; for in the days of the agricultural King Ti, who is supposed to date back to the Fifth Dynasty, that is some five thousand years in the dim past, there is a representation of a plough in use with two handles, very much the same in shape as those brought out quite lately and known as the "American chilled," these being guided in our own old familiar way.

The Baulk wood used as a harrow or roller is drawn by two bullocks, and answers its purpose in smoothing the very sandy soil fairly well.

The Ridging Box, or Baitana, is used for raising low ridges on the flat to retain the water for irrigation purposes.

The Scraper is a box with two handles for levelling high land and earning the sand to lower portions.

RIDGING BOX, OR BAITANA.

The Norag is a massive frame fitted with three or four axles, upon which are fixed steel discs twenty inches in diameter and with four or five discs alternately on each axle. This is drawn by a pair of bullocks over the cut grain till it is threshed out. This implement is, by long proof, most effectual in its action, for when drawn over the grain sheaves it acts in a two-fold way, loosening the ear, or, in the cases of some leguminous crops, the pods—and, of course, vastly helped by the treading of the oxen's hoofs—so that the grain falls through right to the bottom and is covered by fresh quantities, sheaves, or the like, of the crop that is being threshed. Its second action is that the edges of the discs are constantly bruising and half cutting the straw or stalks, which in a dry season or from want of effective irrigation are often hard and woody. It must be understood that the straw is not used; as in England, for litter, but as the most important food for cattle, and this action of the Norag, with its sharp discs, so bruises and chops up the straw that it becomes softened in its harshness, and far better for the animals to which it is supplied for food. In fact, during the time when it is most supplied to the cattle, which is during the summer or least abundant season, it is a work of necessity to make it more attractive to the animals, this bruising and cutting bringing forth the flavour of such juices as still remain in the plant, making it slightly aromatic and certainly more palatable as food.

THE **SCRAPER.**

81

IRRIGATING AFTER USE OF THE BAITANA.

We in England have not been ignorant of the value in cattle feeding of endeavouring to give some zest to the coarser kinds of fodder which economy necessitates in the case of the British farmer. Poor hay, musty grain, consequent upon a bad harvest, and unsatisfying chaff, are eaten by unfortunate cattle, which, suffering as it were from Hobson's choice of having that or none, eat the provender supplied without protest; but Nature resents it for them, and they show it in their poor condition. Of course, in the case of a well-bred horse the matter is different; he snuffs at and blows upon the untempting contents of his manger, and then turns away in disgust from that which his cloven-hoofed companions patiently chew.

THE NORAG.

But in many a case this damaged grain, hay, or straw has been made attractive by a sprinkle of one of the savoury cattle foods that were invented and imitated some forty or fifty years ago, a portion of the ingredients in one kind consisting of the broken up and stickily sweet locust bean and the contents of its pod, with a dash of the bitter and aromatic fenugreek. But in Egypt, where the rain does so little towards injuring the straw or stalk, such musty fare seldom falls to the lot of the native cattle, while this chopped or bruised straw, the *tibn* already mentioned, is constantly prepared at the time of threshing by the action of the ingeniously constructed Norag.

No one can see the spot laid down for the reception of the harvest produce in Egypt—so much hard-beaten earth upon which the peas, beans, or grain of various sorts are thrown, ready for the oxen to drag over it this peculiar revolving wheeled or disked implement—without being reminded of the place where the plague was stayed—the threshing-floor of Araunah the Jebusite; nor can he help comparing the native plough, that simple scarifier, with antique agricultural tillers of the soil depicted on the most ancient sculpture or penned in olden manuscripts, as in use by ancient nations as well as by our Saxon ancestors. The ploughs of the West many, many centuries back are almost precisely the same as those we see in the Egypt of to-day, save in the cases where he who drives the plough has to deal with a hard and heavy earth crust far different to the light and sandy soil of Egypt, whose labourer guides a plough with one hand; for in one antique representation of ploughing the labourer steers the agricultural implement with his left and wields in his right a heavy axe, whose purpose is to break the clods prior to the passing of the implement he steers.

Ingeniously constructed, but that is all that can be said of the native threshing machine, for amongst the poorer class cultivators its manufacture is almost inconceivably rough, and clumsy in the extreme. No verbal description could compete with that afforded by the photo-engraving that accompanies these pages, depicting, as it does, the rough, effective implement, its attendants with their quaint forks and rakes, and, above all, the driver, who adds his weight to the farming implement and shoulders his very merciful speed-inducing wand for the benefit of his mixed yoke. This is, of course, an awkward team, but not infrequent; and the Egyptian farmer who first attempted this application of force must have been as eccentric as he was ingenious when he coupled on either side of such a rough pole a patient camel and a native bull.

THE THRESHING FLOOR.

But somehow, and by a careful division of labour and adjustment of the yoke, the two patient beasts may be seen plodding on round and round the smooth, level, modern representative of the old Biblical threshing-floor. The more regular yoke attached to the Norag, which from its cutting and bruising qualities has been translated by the French "Hache paille," or chop-straw—this bears astounding similarity to the "whop-straw" shared by the old-fashioned British bucolic with his flail—is seen in the other photograph of the pair of native cows, though very frequently it is drawn by a yoke of oxen, by the big, clumsy buffaloes, or even by a yoke consisting of one of each, the oxen taking the palm for their sturdiness and staying power. This mode of threshing and bruising and chopping the straw is carried out in a similar mode in parts of India.

Here though these old ways are giving place to the use of modern machinery, which is readily adopted by the Egyptian, who naturally does not find in the threshing machine the old failing complained of by the British farmer, to wit, that it bruised and broke up the straw, rendering it unfit to use as thatching or to make into the neat, pale golden trusses once so familiar in the market.

There is, however, an unpleasant feature in the native threshing in connection with the samples of corn. As may be supposed, when the threshing is at an end and the *tibn* stacked, or rather piled in a heap, leaving the grain to be shovelled up, no amount of winnowing and sifting can remove from it a certain amount of sullying brought about by the constant trampling of the oxen.

This has, in the past, acted inimically to the success of the fine, hard, dry, shot-like grain of Egypt in foreign markets; but in these days of advance not only has the bullock-worked European threshing machine made its way into the Egyptian fields, but it is no uncommon thing for the pleasant hum of the steam thresher to be heard where the ingenious machinery of England is carrying on its untiring labour of threshing out, winnowing, and filling its sacks of grain, as much at home as if it were upon some Yorkshire or Lincolnshire farm.

It will not be out of place, after dealing with the Egyptian *tibn*, to state here that experienced cultivators have found the advantage of carefully feeding their working bullocks so as to obtain for them the good, sound stamina which will be naturally followed by the best amount of work. This they find by sprinkling amongst the chopped straw or *tibn* supplied about one-third in weight of beans, not crushed or ground, but either whole or split; for it has been noticed that the draught animals flourish better upon this food than upon bean meal; while the process of splitting, Mr Wallace states, saves the bean from the attack of one of the Egyptian farmer's minor plagues—the weevil; for, as if governed by some wondrous instinct in their preparations for the continuation of their species, and a desire to ensure for them good wholesome food upon which to feed, these creatures do not lay their eggs in damaged grain.

Of late years many of the European implements have been introduced —Ransomes' threshers and straw—bruisers, one-way or balance ploughs, harrows, clod-crushers, horse-hoes, Norwegian harrows, spring-tooth cultivators, steam ploughs and cultivators, mowers, reapers, and binders, maize-shellers, seed graders, broadcast-sowing machines, and seed drills.

European ploughs, as they invert the earth, are naturally the most beneficial to the growth of the crop, as by bringing the under-soil to the surface to receive benefit from the sun and air, they greatly improve the root range of the plants.

Steam ploughing is gradually gaining in favour, owing to the scarcity of work-bullocks. A few of the large proprietors have recently purchased plants or entire gear. The scythe for cutting clover has been found, too, a great improvement upon the antique native fashion of pulling by hand, the saving of expense being seventy per cent. But a great drawback to the adoption of European implements is the aversion of the Egyptian farm labourer to any innovation, his want of intelligence in handling what to him appears complicated machinery, and his unwillingness to learn. Here, though, in common justice it must be said that he does not stand alone, for the experiences of the British farmer in most of our counties, and his battles with the pig-headed conservatism of his men, would form an amusing chronicle. The clumsy implement of his forefathers, invented, historians say, some five thousand years ago, is in the native's eyes perfectly right, and could not be better; and he prefers to go on blistering or hardening his hands in what he looks upon as the good old ways, until he is forced to handle modern machines, and then by very, very slow degrees he begins to see, but not before he has broken many, or put them out of gear. But unfortunately the farm labourer is not the sole offender, as the history of the introduction of mechanism of any kind will tell.

Chapter Sixteen.

Much has been written about Egypt and its soil; but in giving here an account of its possibilities and prospects for cultivation in the ways of modern farming, some repetition is necessary. It is fair to say that the soil of Egypt is one of the richest in the world. It is alluvial, ranging from the heavy argillaceous to light loam. It varies, too, in its fertility, and in low-lying lands is frequently impregnated with salt. This is generally owing to want of drainage. When properly treated and flooded with water it soon becomes what is technically known as "sweet," and available for the growth of crops.

Very rich soils are to be found in the provinces of Menoufieh and Charkieh, while those of Beherah are flat and generally low-lying; but the depth may range up to forty feet!

The preparation of the land for the various crops is not what may be termed difficult, although in the heavy black lands powerful draught oxen are required for the ploughs and other implements. But with irrigation at command, and abundance of moisture becoming more and more common in connection with the modern dams and canals, if the land be hard and baked it can be flooded with water as required, when it quickly becomes in a friable condition, and hence comparatively easy to break up.

In the Delta such conditions are never experienced as frequently are encountered upon the heavy clays in England, where the land becomes so hard that it cannot be tilled.

Possessing the qualities of richness, vast depth of soil, and a glorious climate, it is not surprising that with the steady developments of the Khedive's country and the safety and security enjoyed under his enlightened rule, accompanied by the example he is setting in his experiments for the advancement of Egyptian agriculture, the price of land has risen enormously. Within the last few years one hundred pounds per acre is quite a common figure; but that which is unreclaimed can still be purchased for from fifteen to thirty pounds. This, of course, necessitates an additional outlay, which is, after all, quite a moderate sum, upon improvements, when it will yield a good return of profit.

The Egyptian agriculturist divides *his* year into *three* portions:

Summer, from April 1st to August 1st.

Nileh, from August 1st to December 1st.

Winter, from December 1st to April 1st. But it must be remembered that the Egyptian winter would be better named balmy spring.

As this little work is written primarily for those who take an interest in the progress of a favoured country, and who may possibly be looking towards the East with the eyes of investment, or for a future home where they may lead a Virgilian or bucolic life, it is proposed to give here a simple, business-like account of the various processes and preparations made for the growth and harvesting of the different crops sown in the above seasons:—

Winter Crops: Clover, barley, beans, and wheat.

Summer Crops: Cotton and sugar-cane, and also maize.

Nileh Crop: Maize alone.

Rotation.—A three years' rotation is the one generally practised, although there is a tendency to limit it to two years.

It would be as well to consider the crops as they succeed each other, beginning with the cotton.

A great deal of interest attaches to the growth of cotton in Egypt. It was largely cultivated by the ancient Egyptians, and its products utilised, but after a time—it is impossible to say how long, possibly during the great changes that took place during incursions, conquests, or change of rulers—its growth died out to such an extent that a few generations back, as an article of utility, its cultivation had pretty well ceased, and cotton was scarcely known, save as a decorative shrub in the gardens of Cairo.

But during the reign of the Khedive's ancestor, Mehemet Ali, a man of great foresight, full of determination for the advance of his people, he completely grasped the idea that Egypt was one of the most suitable of countries for the cultivation of the cotton tree, and that it ought to be produced in his dominions instead of dependence being placed upon importation from other lands.

In pursuance of this idea, he began to make experiments, testing it, so to speak, by forming plantations. These turned out so well that he proceeded to take further steps, and with great enterprise commenced the cultivation upon a large scale. Many thousands of the Egyptian acres were planted in the lower provinces, and to a far greater extent planting was carried on in the rich lands of Upper Egypt bordering on the Nile.

The little trees responded freely to the Egyptian cultivation; the rich, irrigated soil, yearly replenished by the sediment left by the floods, proved that the ancients were right, and wherever the land was deep the results were most favourable; while where a bad selection had been made, and the soil was shallow and inferior, the return of the pods, or technically *bolls*, was poor.

The method of its cultivation will be given *in extenso* farther on, but it will be as well to note here, in regard to the enterprise which turned Egypt into its present state as one of the great cotton-growing countries of the world, that the seed was originally imported from Brazil, though it is undoubtedly a native of Northern Africa; and at the present time the returns are very great.

The preparation of the land for the growth of cotton commences in January. The seed is sown from the middle of February till the middle of March, and the cropping harvested, or picked, about the end of November; while previous to the last picking of the soft woolly pods, clover seed is sown amongst the standing cotton trees.

This, so to speak, stolen crop provides a supply for horses, cattle, and sheep till the end of June; for it must be borne in mind that Egypt is not a land of fields and meadows enclosed by hedgerows; hence grazing for cattle is the result of foresight, and has to be provided as required.

On the land not sown with clover, and at the end of the cotton harvest, after the little trees have been uprooted, a crop of beans is sown, which becomes ready for harvesting in April; and now there is a period in which the agriculturist may take his choice of sowing what may be termed catch crops, or fallowing his land for five months. In this he is guided by position and the facility offered for the disposal of such easy crops as water melons or maize, which can be taken after beans.

It is at the end of October that he begins to think of his main crops, when wheat and barley are sown, to be harvested from the beginning of May to the end of June. Then follows the main crop of maize, which occupies the land from July 15th to November 15th.

Previous to the harvesting of this main crop of maize, clover is again sown, and from this one or two pasturings are obtained before the land is broken up once more for the succeeding important crop of cotton, this completing the rotation.

The sugar-cane has not been given a place in this rotation, as it is principally grown in Upper Egypt for the manufacture of sugar, while we are dealing with the rich lands of the Delta and the farming there. But we may here remark that the Egyptians are as fond of the green sugar-cane as an article of diet as the blacks of the West Indies, who may be seen munching its luscious saccharine at all times and seasons.

There is something more in this among the Egyptians than the gratification of a sweet palate, for it is eaten largely from the great faith of rich and poor alike in its tonic qualities. "Gasab," or as they pronounce it in Cairo "'asab," is considered to be one of the greatest restorers for those who from weak health or excess are what we call in modern phraseology "run down"—perhaps as pleasant, plentiful, and economical a medicament as could be used. It is a common sight for the European to see the poor, patient, overladen, and underfed donkeys coming into Cairo every morning heavily laden with the juicy caries that have been grown in the neighbouring fields.

It will be observed in the above rotation that a crop of clover precedes and succeeds the cotton.

We now proceed to a technical statement of the treatment of an Egyptian farm; not merely a description of farming in Egypt, but of the management of a farm based upon the careful observations of one who has passed many years in the Delta and has made the cultivation and cropping of its peculiar soil a thorough life study. In fact, the tracts of land under his superintendence offer themselves as specimens worthy of copying by all who seek to make the land of Egypt profitable and well paying in return for the capital, large or small, that may be invested there. This being said, we at once plunge again *in medias res*, and, at the risk of being too formal and technical, recapitulate the crops in their order. Cotton.

Followed by Clover, or Beans, or both.

Followed by Fallow, or catch crops of Maize or Water Melons.

Wheat and Barley.

Followed by three months' fallow, or Maize, main crop, and catch crop of Sesame. Clover—"Fachl" on land after Maize and Clover "Miscowy" after Fallow. Then Cotton.

Chapter Seventeen.

We will take an estate of three hundred acres, and on inspection, say in the month of March, the crops occupying the land under the following rotation will be as under:—

Three Years' Rotation. March.

100 Acres Cotton
50 acres Clover
50 acres Beans
80 acres Wheat
20 acres Barley

Two Years' Rotation. March.

150 Acres Cotton
30 acres Clover
40 acres Beans
60 acres Wheat
20 acres Barley

Within the last few years there has been a tendency to increase the cotton crop and adopt the two years' rotation; but it is not a good practice, as it tends to exhaustion of the soil, especially where there is a want of farmyard manure. The cereal crops also suffer from the consequent lateness of sowing.

Two crops off the same land per annum: Wheat, sown November 15th, harvested May 30th; maize, sown July 15th and harvested November 15th. Or clover, sown November 1st, first crop January 1st, 3 pounds; second crop March 15th, 3 pounds. Sow cotton in end of March. Ground clear, November. Probable gross return per acre, 24 pounds.

We might multiply instances where two separate crops can be grown on the same land in twelve months, such as maize followed by potatoes, etc.; but it may be safely stated that a very small area of a well-appointed farm is allowed to lie fallow, the land being continually under some crop or another.

A few remarks on the before-mentioned crops as to cultivation:—

Cotton is the principal crop in the rotation, and gives far the best monetary return, while at the present time reports from the Egyptian Soudan are beginning to speak very highly of the alluvial tracts between the White and Blue Niles as being more favourable to the growth of cotton than the lower portions of the Nile Valley, while affording ten times the area for the planting of this important staple that can be had in the lower portions of the Delta. In fact, matters seem to prove that Upper Egypt is going to develop into the finest cotton-growing country in the world.

The preparation commences in January, and generally three ploughings are required to bring the land into a proper tilth. The more thorough the cultivation the better for the crop. The land is then thrown into ridges measuring from crest to crest three feet. Then a pair of ridges is drawn across the longitudinal ridges, the distance between each pair of ridges (which form a waterway) being twenty-two yards. Between these pairs—*i.e.* eleven yards distance from each—a single ridge is made. This acts as a partition to stop the water. Six ridges are irrigated by allowing the water to flow from these cross-waterways, and the reason for confining the length of the ridges to eleven yards is to ensure the evenness of the irrigation as to height of water level, as the ground may have slight fall, and if the whole length of the ridges were to be watered at once the water would rise too high at the lower parts before the higher levels were properly soaked.

The sowing commences February 15th. Boys and girls drop the seed in clusters of, say, twelve seeds in set-holes made by a pointed stick on one side of the ridge, two-thirds from the bottom of the furrow, and at a distance of sixteen inches between each set-hole.

After "planting," the ridges are watered, care being taken not to allow the water to rise to the level of the seed. Sufficient moisture for germination is derived from capillarity. The seeds shoot and the plants appear above ground in from ten to twelve days. Twenty-five days elapse, and then a light hand-hoeing is given, while after fifteen days more the plants are thinned, two or three being allowed to remain in each set-hole.

Immediately after thinning the young plants receive their first watering. After, say, twelve days a second hand-hoeing is given, and again after twelve days a third. Then comes the second watering, by means of trench and canal. After an interval of ten days another hand-hoeing is given, and this finishes the task, as the cotton trees have attained a height which precludes the possibility of using the implement.

At intervals of from ten to fifteen days six waterings are given. This brings the grower to the time—about September 10th—when the crop is ready for the first picking. Women, boys, and girls pluck the cotton from the trees. Eight to twelve of the workers may pick an acre per day, and they receive as payment one shilling per 100 pounds. At the conclusion of the picking the field is irrigated again, and after twenty-five days the second crop is dealt with. Another irrigation follows, time is given for development, and then comes the third and last picking.

The cotton trees are next cut close to the ground or pulled up by the roots, and are utilised as fuel.

An average crop on good land may produce 1,890 pounds of raw cotton, which on being ginned will yield 600 pounds of fibre. The raw cotton—*i.e.* in seed—is sold per 375 pounds at, say, 3 pounds. This will gin out, say, 105 pounds fibre and 205 pounds seed; so that the total worth of the crop may be estimated at 18 pounds, exclusive of the value of the wood, which may be placed at 4 shillings per acre. These figures are often exceeded where the cultivation is well attended to.

Cost of raising one acre of cotton in Egypt.

	pounds s. d.
Three Ploughings	0 12 0
One Ridging	0 4 0
Dressing Ridges	0 2 0
Planting	0 0 10
Seed	0 5 0
Wages for Nine Irrigations	0 5 6
Six Irrigations by Pump	0 15 0
Three Irrigations by Free Flow	0 0 0
Three Cultivations by Hoe	0 7 0
Three Pickings	1 0 0
Pulling Trees	0 3 0
	3 pounds 14 4
Farmyard Manure and Application	0 10 0
Total	4 4 4

The varieties of cotton grown in Lower Egypt are Mit-Afifi, Abbassi, Yannovitch; in Upper Egypt, Ashmouni.

Generally speaking, the quality of Egyptian cotton is of a high grade. Its fibre is long, fine, and at the same time strong.

Unfortunately this country has pests, not like the old Biblical plagues, but which give much trouble and do a certain amount of damage to the cotton crop. Among these are the cotton caterpillar and the boll-worm, the former being propagated from eggs deposited by a moth, which do great damage if allowed to hatch, by the larva feeding upon the plant. If the leaves upon which the eggs are deposited are pulled and burned, this mitigates the destruction so far as it is successfully carried out. The boll-worm bores into and feeds upon the heart of the young bolls, and thereby totally destroys them for the production of fibre. Up to the present no remedy has been found to prevent the ravages of these pests. The damage may amount to 20 per cent. Fogs and dews in the month of October also cause injury to the bolls.

Beans after Cotton.—This crop may be sown at any time during the month of November, the earlier the better. The beans may be either sown broadcast or dropped into the furrow, behind the native plough. The quantity of seed required is two and a half bushels. The land must be very moist, or an irregular germination of the seed will be the result. The crop receives the first watering thirty days after sowing, or immediately before flowering, and again when the beans have formed in the pod. Harvest will commence about the middle of April. Men, women, and boys pull the crop by hand, breaking the stalks close to the ground, sometimes uprooting them, but a small serrated hook is also used to cut the stalks. Six hands will reap one acre per day, and the payment is in kind, at the rate of one sheaf per thirty. The crop is then carted to the threshing-floor, spread out to dry, and threshed by the Norag; or, as modern implements are creeping into use, by a steam threshing machine made by one of the famous English firms.

This crop does not receive any manure, but requires a rich, heavy soil, when under favourable conditions a yield may be expected of from twenty-five to thirty-five bushels per acre—price per five bushels, 1 pound. Occasionally this crop is damaged by hot blasts—"Khamsin winds"—which shrivel the bean, especially if they occur when it is soft. We have also the pest of broomrape; and if badly infested by this weed, great destruction follows to the crop. Beans are the main feed of working bullocks, milch cows, and donkeys.

Catch crops, on land after beans.

Maize (summer).—Sown end of April, ready to be pulled after sixty days. This crop is consumed by the natives, who roast the cobs. Cost of raising one acre, 2 pounds 10 shillings, exclusive of rent. Gross value of crop may be approximately 10 pounds.

Water Melons.—Sown at the same date, ripe after eighty days. Cost of raising, 3 pounds 10 shillings. Probable value of the produce of an acre, 12 pounds. After these crops have been harvested the land is fallowed for three months. During the fallow it receives two or three ploughings, and is flooded with water to prepare it for sowing the cereal crops.

Egyptian Clover (*Trifolium Alexandrinum*).—After Cotton.—This crop may be termed the preserver of Egyptian agriculture, since, as previously alluded to, it provides pasturage for horses, cattle, sheep, camels, mules, and donkeys, for a period of seven months, and also taking into account its beneficial effects on the soil, restoring fertility by root residue containing nitrogen. Sown in the end of October amongst the standing cotton trees, the seed falls upon the newly irrigated soil and takes root, no covering being required. Sixty pounds of seed is sufficient for an acre. The first crop should be ready for pasturing at the beginning of January; second crop, seventy-five days; third crop, forty days; fourth crop, thirty-five days' interval.

This variety is named "Miscowy," and stands copious watering. The first and second crops contain about eighty per cent, of moisture. The third crop may be made into hay, and the fourth crop—part only—may be threshed to furnish seed. The gross weight of the four crops, cut green, may be estimated at thirty tons, or five tons of hay. The work-bullocks, cows, buffaloes, horses, etc., are tethered by a rope attached to their fore-legs and fixed to a peg driven into the ground, the cattlemen moving the animals forward as required. The cattle lie out at night while pasturing on the clover.

If the crop of clover is near a large town where dairymen require green pasture, the price per feddan, to be consumed on the land, may be put at 4 pounds, 3 pounds, 3 pounds 10 shillings, 3 pounds 10 shillings for the four crops, or a total of 14 pounds. Growers are sometimes troubled by attacks of cut-worms, which ravage the young shoots of clover; but flooding with water often destroys the pest. There is also the parasitic weed Dodder (*Cuscuta Trifolii*), which occasionally does damage to the crop. The cost of five bushels of clover seed varies from one pound 10 shillings to 3 pounds 10 shillings, according to supply and demand. The variety "Fachl" clover occupies a separate place in the rotation, and will be treated later.

Wheat.—Varieties: Common wheat, Bocchi, and Indian. The Bocchi, a white wheat, is extensively grown. The third, a reddish wheat, has recently been introduced from India, and gives good crops. Egyptian wheats are hard, but are deficient in albuminoids. Unfortunately, care is not taken in selecting the seed, and many samples are badly mixed with red and white varieties. The crop is sown on fallow land after clover and beans. The land, previous to sowing the seed, has received a watering. Fifteen to twenty days after, the seed—two and a half bushels—is sown broadcast, and is ploughed in by the native plough. The sowing is very often imperfectly performed, the distribution of the seed being very irregular. The next process is rolling by drawing a baulk of wood (see illustration), three yards long, over the land; then ridges are made seven yards apart to regulate the even distribution of water.

Somewhere about twelve days after the sowing the shoots appear above ground, when the "braird" is about four inches high. Occasionally there is an attack of "grub," or cut-worm; but the damage is never serious, a watering destroying the pest, and some seed sown on the blanks caused by the worm soon make good the damage. Rolling with a press roller has been found to materially stop the destruction. Eighty days after sowing, or when the crop has attained a height of two feet, it receives its first watering; forty days afterwards its second and last. Sixty days after the final irrigation the crop will be ripe for harvest. The method of harvesting—reaping—is by small hand hooks, men, women, and boys turning out to work at midnight, reaping till seven a.m., subsequently gathering the unbound sheaves into rows, and afterwards gleaning, finishing up about nine a.m.

The foremen then distribute to the reapers one sheaf for thirty-five, as payment in kind. The reason for reaping the crop by night is that, if performed in the daytime, while the heat is great, the grain would shed, the dews at night preventing this loss. Reaping by self-binders has been tried, but the shedding of grain was excessive, as they could only be worked in the daytime; while the farm labourer was not qualified to work such a complicated machine. Labour is so cheap that it is not necessary to resort to labour-saving machinery. The sheaves (unbound) are transported from the fields to the threshing-floor by camels, carts drawn by oxen, or mules. The sheaves are then placed in a circle measuring twenty yards in diameter. Four, five, or more pairs of oxen, each pair attached to a Norag, circle round on the top of the grain, and when it has been threshed out and the straw cut and bruised by the revolving discs and the feet of the oxen, it is thrown into a heap in the centre. Fresh sheaves are added to the circle as they arrive. When all the grain has been threshed the next process is the winnowing by throwing the cut straw and grain into the air vertically by means of a five-pronged wooden fork. The cut straw, *Tibn*, is carried by the wind to a distance, while the grain falls near to the operator.

FOREMAN OF FELLAHEEN.

The payment to the winnower is at the rate of fourpence per five bushels. Threshing and finishing machines, made in England, similar to the one illustrated, are used on all the large estates, and perform the work quicker and cheaper than the Norag, and of course they are much cleaner, the straw not being trampled and defiled. They are complicated, owing to the fact that the straw must be chopped and rendered soft to the touch, as the oxen will not eat it when it is not bruised—a serious matter, this, in a country where cattle are almost entirely fed upon straw. It might be argued that, as in England, the wheat and other stalks might be cut up by machinery into chaff; but the explanation is simple. The haulm or stalk of cereals in a hot country like Egypt grows harder and more woody than that of colder climates, and when simply cut up into chaff the product is so harsh that the unfortunate animals find that it soon produces soreness of the mouth, and reject it in consequence as being unfit for food. The sample of grain after being threshed by the Norag is often, however, mixed with particles of earth, as some of the crop has been pulled up by the roots.

But as most of the wheat is consumed in the country the people do not object to a dirty sample.

The total value of one of these crops may be taken at nine pounds 10 shillings per acre. The cost of raising one acre of wheat, ploughing, labour, watering, up till harvesting, may be estimated at one pound 10 shillings, and the yield may be thirty-five bushels grain and one and a half tons straw. The weight of grain per imperial bushel is sixty-four pounds, and the price per five bushels one pound. Algerian and Italian wheats have been tried, and the results have been fairly encouraging. English varieties have also been experimented with, but invariably have resulted in failure through bad germination.

Barley.—The native variety, Baladi, is mainly grown. The head is four-rowed, and about two and a half inches long. It is sown in November and December. Seeding, the same as for wheat. Seed, two bushels per acre. First watering, sixty days after sowing; second and last watering, fifty days after the first. Harvest commences April 15th. Reaping the same as for wheat. Cost of raising one acre, one pound 5 shillings. Yield of a good average crop, sixty bushels grain and one and a quarter tons straw. The weight of grain per bushel is fifty-seven pounds, and the price ten shillings per five bushels. Total value per acre, 7 pounds 10 shillings. The barley is fed to horses mules, donkeys, and camels, while the natives make it into bread after mixing it with wheat in equal proportions. Egyptian barley grown in the Delta is not good for malting purposes, the grain not being "plump." In 1893, by way of experiment, a few foreign varieties were grown in Egypt, principally with a view to providing a good malting sample.

Scotch Chevalier barley gave the best results. A sample from the crop of 1895, grown from seed raised in the country, was awarded the first prize for barley grown out of England at the Brewers' Exhibition, London.

The yield was not so heavy as with native barley, being as eight is to twelve; but it furnished more straw. The money value in England was Chevalier, 1 pound 9 shillings, as compared to 17 shillings for native barley; but the European barleys are more difficult to grow, and if not reaped before becoming dead ripe the heads break off and fall to the ground.

Barley is grown on the Libyan Desert (Mariout), west from Alexandria, and is entirely dependent on the rains in winter. It is sown by the Bedouins in October—to await the rains which may fall in November or December—and also after a rainfall. As the Bedouin is not an agriculturist, he scatters one and a quarter bushels per acre, and scratches the ground by the aid of a small plough, to which is yoked a camel or donkey.

This soil is of a rich yellow colour, sandy loam, fine level tracts of it extending to a thousand acres or more. To obtain a good supply of water, wells are dug to a depth of forty feet or so, and the supply is fairly good. Perennial irrigation can be resorted to by means of these wells.

If the rains are propitious, the Bedouin may reap crops of barley, with extremely varied returns, running, as they do, from two and a half to twenty bushels per acre, the price received on the spot being 15 shillings per five bushels. Ninety per cent, of the barley goes to England for malting.

Next come, in the rotation,

Maize (Nileh).—Main crop on land after cereal crops. Sown end of July. Seed, about one bushel per acre, dropped in the furrow by a boy immediately behind the plough. First watering, twenty-five days after sowing; second fifteen days after; third twelve days, fourth twelve days, fifth ten days, sixth eight days, and seventh eight days, seven irrigations being necessary in this dry and thirsty land for the production of the crop. One cultivation is given by hand hoe after the first watering. The maize grows quickly, attaining to a height of seven feet, and occupies the ground one hundred days. Cost of raising, two pounds 6 shillings. Yield per acre, fifty bushels; value, 8 pounds 10 shillings.

Maize is a most important crop in Egypt, as upon this grain the natives depend for the bulk of their food. Ground into flour and mixed with Fenugreek seed, it is baked into bread. Five varieties of this grain are grown, but the best kinds are known by the natives as "Baladi," "Biltani," and "Nab-el-Gamal." As Indian corn is a surface feeder a liberal application of farmyard manure is necessary to secure a full crop. Harvest begins in the middle of November. The stalks are cut and carted to the threshing-floor. Then the cobs are pulled from the stalks and spread out to dry for thirty days, when they are put into the granaries. To separate the grain from the cobs, hand shellers are employed, or it is beaten out by sticks.

For a catch crop on land after wheat and barley, Sesame may be sown in the beginning of June. There are two varieties, the Red and the White. Six pounds of seed will sow one acre, broadcasted and ploughed in by the native implement. The duration of the growth is five months. The crop receives one hand-hoeing and five waterings. It is harvested in October before it becomes dead ripe, to prevent the shedding of seed. Sesame is grown for the sake of the oil, which it yields to the extent of over fifty per cent. This oil is used for domestic purposes, especially by the upper class Egyptians. The production of seed per acre is about twenty-five bushels, valued at 13 pounds.

In some parts of Upper Egypt a great deal of land is sown with the Dourra (*Holcus douta*), which is largely consumed by the peasantry, forming, as it does, one of their staple foods. It is a very useful and suitable plant. It is sometimes eaten like maize or Indian corn in a green state, being previously roasted on the fire, or green like sugar-cane. Its pith, when dried, is used as starch; while the leaves make excellent provender for cattle.

We now have to consider the last crop in the rotation, namely clover preceding cotton. As part of the land after wheat and barley has remained fallow, and advantage has been taken to level, clean, and flood with Nile water rich in deposits, "Miscowy" clover is sown broadcast, when the surface of the land is covered with three inches of water. As the water sinks into the soil the seed germinates upon the surface, which is now composed of fine silt. Sown in the middle of September, the first crop should be ready for cutting or pasturing about November 5th. During the period of growth the crop has received three waterings. Immediately after the clearing a watering is given, and the second cutting should be ready in seventy days. After eating off, the land is ploughed for the cotton crop.

ON THE NILE.

"Fachl" clover is stronger in the stem than that known as "Miscowy," and grows as a tall, luxuriant crop. It is sown amongst the stalks of the maize in the end of October, the land having previously been watered, and by the time the maize is ready for cutting, the clover has attained a height of five inches. The crop should be ready for cutting about the middle of January. Generally it is disposed of by the acre—to be cut and removed from the land, and sold in bunches to be fed to carriage horses, precisely as the green tares and clover are brought into London in bunches during the spring time of the year. The value of one cutting is 5 pounds per acre. Unlike the "Miscowy" variety, the "Fachl" only yields one crop, as the roots fail. The land is then broken up for the crop of cotton. This finishes the three years' rotation.

Chapter Eighteen.

It will be interesting to add a few remarks on a system of cultivation which is practised on tracts adjoining the Desert. The land has been purchased at a price of, say, 17 pounds per acre, and the next proceeding has been to level it—by the free use of the Cassabia, or scraper, which, in roughest preparation, is drawn over and over the sand and guided something after the fashion of a plough—and then bringing it into communication by canalising with the nearest distributor of the Nile water, while in this country of exceedingly cheap labour the cost of these preparations for cultivation may be set down at about 10 pounds per acre.

This done, the purchaser has the option of carrying on the cultivation himself, or letting it to the fellaheen, who will take it readily and pay a rent of 4 pounds per acre or feddan.

The fellah now crops his land as follows, and the reader will notice the variation in the products the native causes his fields to bring forth.

He begins with:

Earth Nuts (*Arachidis*).—Sown from April 1st till July 1st. Duration of crops, six months. Water every five days till high Nile, when no water is required. Yield per acre, sixty bushels, value 10 pounds.

Sesame.—Yield, fifteen bushels; value, 7 pounds.

Chick Peas.—Sown from April 1st to July 1st. Duration of crop, six months. Yield per acre, thirty bushels; value, 6 pounds.

Maize (Oswego).—Sown March 15th till April 15th. Duration of crop, seven months; value of crop, 9 pounds.

Potatoes.—First crop planted October. Duration, three and a half months. Yield, three and a half tons; 17 pounds 10 shillings.

Potatoes.—Second crop planted February 15th. Duration, three months. Yield, three and a half tons; 17 pounds 10 shillings.

Lupins.—Sown November 1st. Duration of crop, seven months.

Average yield, fifteen bushels; 2 pounds 8 shillings.

Clover, barley, beans, Syrian maize, and henna, a dye plant.

To begin with, the land is here generally pure sand, but after flooding with Nile water, which is often available without pumping—*i.e.* free flow —the sand gets mixed with the Nile mud and a good soil is rapidly formed.

Sugar-Cane.—This, one of the most interesting products of the Eastern soil, beautiful in form, and attractive in every stage, from its early green growth through the tasselling, or flowering, up to the time when the swelling cobs are changing from their attractive green to golden yellow, amber, and brownish or purple black, is cultivated both in Upper and Lower Egypt. It is grown in two varieties, the native and the Greek, and the colour of the ripened canes forms a gradation, passing from light yellow through striped red and yellow, and red.

The cultivation is, as stated, principally carried on in Upper Egypt—for the manufacture of sugar. If it is planted in the Delta it is for sale to the natives, by whom it is consumed raw, and by sucking the juice. The farmer who plants his land with sugar-cane begins by thoroughly well preparing the soil, and ridges it as if he were about to plant potatoes, these ridges measuring about thirty inches from crest to crest.

The canes are cut into lengths of one yard, placed in the furrow, and covered with the soil. Planting commences in February, the ridges being watered immediately after, and the young shoots appear after twenty days. The crop is watered every fifteen days, and at longer intervals after the Nile has risen. The land is hand-hoed three times, and the cane should be ready for cutting in December and January. The value of an average crop sold standing—in Lower Egypt—may range from 20 to 25 pounds per acre. Then the trashings covering the ridges are burned, a watering given about the beginning of March, and the old roots sprout again, when there is a second crop, and again the following year by repeating, a third crop from the one planting. The third crop is not so profitable, as the roots become exhausted. The sugar-cane requires a liberal dressing of manure each year. The yield of trashed canes may run from six tons the first year, five tons the second year, and four tons the third year, and the percentage of sugar may be estimated from fourteen to fifteen per cent.

Chapter Nineteen.

Rice is extensively cultivated in the districts of Rosetta, Damietta, Fouah, and Facous; but it is the opinion of a very excellent authority that rice cultivation and the growth of this grain, which is seen at its best in the swamps of Asia, will gradually die out of Egypt and become a thing of the past. For, given ample water and a level of mud in which the planter may thrust in the plant in its early green state of blades, an abundant crop is pretty sure; but now that Egypt is becoming more and more in a state of transition, with good drainage extending, and modern applications at work for the proper washing and purifying of a soil that is impregnated with salt and soda, this country will no longer be the paddy field of yore, and the culture of rice may well be relegated to the mud swamps of the countries farther east.

There is no cause for regret here, for, in comparison with those easier of production, rice is far from being one of the best crops that can be sown. Among farmers and gardeners there is a term known as sickness of the land, marked by a want of vigour in its productions; and in Egypt this may be produced by the want of that great sustainer of plant life, decaying vegetable matter, or the impregnation of the soil with some form of salt, soda in the main.

With the improved farming now going on, the natural soil, which was once ready enough in its production of rice, is rapidly changing its character, constant tillage, the flooding and washing which carry out the efflorescing salts, and the constant addition of vegetable manures, aided by one or two crops of clover, being the agents which are working this alteration.

There are five varieties of rice grown in Egypt, namely Sultani, Fino, Sabeini, Indian, and Japan. In regard to quality, the Fino occupies the first place.

The sowing commences in the middle of April, and continues till June. The crop occupies the land from three to six months, according to the variety grown. The rice for seeding is put into water for twelve days, then taken out and drained for two more. It is subsequently emptied out of the sacks on to a floor and covered with hay, to remain four days till heating and germination take place. Then the seed is sown on the land, which is covered with four inches of water, this being drained off after three days, leaving the seed for twelve hours exposed to the sun. Then water is allowed to flow on to the plot once more, and a portion to drain off, the surface at this later stage always having a covering of from four to five inches in depth, so that the irrigation is always fresh. This is continued during the growth of the crop.

The harvesting is in October and November, and the yield of an acre may average fifty bushels of Paddy, which, when shelled, or husked, will give twenty bushels of clean rice, valued at 6 pounds 10 shillings per twenty bushels. The straw may be estimated at a ton per acre, and be valued at one pound per ton.

Rice is one of the chief foods of the Egyptian, and it is an excellent crop to grow on newly redeemed land, provided that water is abundant; for the soil is impregnated with salt, and after a few crops have been taken off the land becomes "sweet," in consequence of the perpetual flooding. It can then be cropped with clover and cotton, but requires much labour in the way of weeding, transplanting to fill up blanks, and attention to irrigation. After paying rent and working expenses the margin of profit is not great. The size of the plots ranges from half to one and a half acres. The patches are encircled by drains or ditches, which discharge into the main irrigating system.

Chapter Twenty.

If armed with the little enterprise and capital necessary for making a commencement in farming or growing fruit and vegetables in Egypt for the market, a cultivator would find that land could be obtained within easy reach of the great towns of the Delta—Cairo and Alexandria—at a very moderate price; but it is only right to add that this price, consequent upon the great irrigation schemes in progress, is still rising by leaps and bounds. For the soil, where reachable by the flood waters of the Nile, now conserved and carried in every direction by irrigation canals, is practically inexhaustible, and, as previously stated, is often of great depth.

The land is to be purchased with proper titles and registration, giving the necessary security to an alien who is desirous of making his home in the Delta, or rented, if preferred, at a moderate consideration, including water for irrigation. The country is well policed, there is freedom from contact with the inhabitants of the surrounding desert, and a cultivator would have to deal with a quiet, docile people, fairly industrious—that is to say, lovers of work after the fashion of the calm, placid Moslem, who takes life as it is, and seems to make it one of his tenets that there is no need to hurry.

He possesses none of the hurry and rush of Western civilisation; but, on the other hand, he is patient, ignorant, fairly teachable, and willing to work for exceedingly moderate daily payment. The supply of this labour under a kindly, solvent, and honestly paying master is abundant and never fails.

The illustrations of the fellaheen farm labourers and their wives are typical of the class of people with whom he would have to deal, and if the new adventurer objected to the class of hut they occupy, and had lofty ideas about model dwellings and the introduction of lighter implements in place of the clumsy, adze-like hoes with which they are armed rather than furnished, the advice given to him would be to follow that of the old Latin proverb, "Festina lente," and go by degrees in that, as in most of the other matters of culture, for it takes time to alter custom and change old-fashioned routine.

It may be here added that all great advance and reversals of custom should be cautiously attempted with the land. Still Nature is easier to deal with than man, and less likely to resent alteration when attempted by a practised hand.

As a whole, for the encouragement of those who wish to try the experiment in a foreign land, let them understand that farming in Egypt is child's play compared to that in Great Britain. There are no wet hay and cereal harvests, there is neither snow nor frost to damage the crops, no high winds, no floods, no ground game to do mischief:

In the season of hay-making, with no possibility of a drop of rain falling, the fellah makes the worst of all hay by allowing it to be burnt to an indigestible fibre—would that he had a training in the uncertain climate of Great Britain! The wheat is harvested when dead ripe. Part may be cut, and part may be allowed to remain for six weeks without deterioration. A contrast this to the harvests in bonnie Scotland, where the corn has lain sodden until it has rotted away in the deplorable weather of the year 1903.

There is a good old proverb that is applicable to most things—certainly to farming in Egypt. It is that "the less there is to do, the worse it is done." Verily it is so here. Nature is most kindly, and with ample moisture, abundant fertilisation, and plenteous sunshine, she does pretty well half of the fellahs' work thoroughly well, while their half to complete the operations is carried out with a careless indifference to success that is deplorable. The people's wants are few, and now that under a generous rule they have liberty and payment for the work they perform, they seem quite content to plod on in easy slothfulness. Sufficient for the day is the evil thereof, so why wear themselves out by toil and the struggle for things better than those which surround them?

All this in connection with the possibilities of this country raises the question, Can the practice of Egyptian agriculture be improved?

The answer of one who has toiled amongst the people for years, whose work has been that of reclaiming tracts of desert land, making endless experiments as to the best suited crops for Egypt and the best ways of producing them, is: Emphatically, yes!

The End.

Lightning Source UK Ltd.
Milton Keynes UK
UKHW041835060820
367830UK00007B/746

9 783752 379990